Junior High

Talksheets

Fifty Creative Discussions for
Junior High Youth Groups

by

David Lynn

Edited by Wayne Rice

Illustrations by Corbin Hillam

ZondervanPublishingHouse
Grand Rapids, Michigan
A Division of HarperCollinsPublishers

JUNIOR HIGH TALKSHEETS

Youth Specialties Books
are published by Zondervan Publishing House
Grand Rapids, Michigan 49530

Copyright © 1988 by Youth Specialties, Inc.

ISBN 0-310-20941-2

All Scripture quotations, unless otherwise noted, are taken from the
HOLY BIBLE: NEW INTERNATIONAL VERSION (North American
Edition). Copyright © 1973, 1978, 1984, by the International Bible
Society. Used by permission of Zondervan Bible Publishers.

Edited by Wayne Rice
Designed by The Church Art Works
Illustrated by Corbin Hillam

Printed in the United States of America

97 98 99 00 01 02 / ❖ ML / 19 18 17 16 15

Junior High

Table of Contents

TABLE OF CONTENTS (continued)

* * * * *

HOW TO USE TALKSHEETS

You have in your possession a very valuable book. It contains 50 instant youth group discussions for junior high school students. Inside, you will find reproducible "TalkSheets" covering a wide variety of "hot topics", plus simple step-by-step instructions on how to use them. All you need for 50 successful youth meetings is this book and a copy machine.

TalkSheets are easy to use and very flexible. They can be used in a youth group meeting, a Sunday School class, or in a Bible study group. They are adaptable for either large or small groups. They can be fully covered in twenty minutes, or more intensively in two hours. You can build an entire youth group meeting around a single TalkSheet, or you can use TalkSheets to supplement other materials and resources you might be using. The choice is yours.

TalkSheets are much more than just another type of curriculum or workbook. They actually get the students involved and excited about discussing important issues and growing in their faith. TalkSheets deal with key topics young people want to talk about. With interesting activities, challenging questions and eye-catching graphics, TalkSheets will capture the attention of your students and help them think and learn. The more often you use TalkSheets, the more your junior high students will look forward to them.

TALKSHEETS ARE DISCUSSION STARTERS

While TalkSheets can be used as curriculum for your youth group, they are primarily designed to be used as discussion starters. Everyone knows the value of a good discussion. In a discussion, young people take part and interact with one another. When they are talking about a specific subject, they are more apt to do some serious thinking about it, to try to understand it better, to formulate and defend their points of view, and to make decisions. Discussion helps truth rise to the surface and helps young people discover it for themselves. There is no better way to promote learning than to encourage good discussion.

A common fear voiced by many junior high youth group leaders is "What will I do if the students in my group just sit there and don't say a word?". This is why many group leaders would rather show a movie or give a lecture.

Usually when students don't have anything to say, it's because they haven't had the time nor the opportunity to get their thoughts organized. Most young people haven't yet developed the ability to "think on their feet". They do not know how to present their ideas and opinions spontaneously, with confidence. They are afraid to open their mouths for fear they might sound stupid.

This is why TalkSheets work so well. TalkSheets give young people a chance to interact with the subject matter in an interesting, challenging and non-threatening way *before* the actual discussion begins. This not only gives them time to organize their thoughts and to write them down, but also reduces any anxiety they might feel about participating. Most students will actually look forward to sharing their answers and finding out how others reponded to the same questions. They will be primed and ready for a lively discussion.

A STEP-BY-STEP USER'S GUIDE

TalkSheets are very easy to use, but do require a minimum of preparation. Follow these simple instructions and you'll have a successful TalkSheet discussion:

1 **Choose the right TalkSheet for your group.** Each TalkSheet deals with a different topic. The one you choose will depend upon the needs and the maturity level of your group. Don't feel obligated to use the TalkSheets in the order in which they appear in this book. They were not intended to be used that way.

2 **Try it yourself.** Once you have chosen a TalkSheet for your group, answer the questions and do the activities yourself. Imagine your students' reactions to the TalkSheet. This will give you first-hand knowledge of what you will be asking your students to do. As you fill out the TalkSheet, think of other appropriate questions, activities and scriptures.

3 **Read the Leader's Instructions (on the back of each TalkSheet).** Included are numerous tips and ideas for getting the most out of your discussion. You may wish to add some of your own thoughts or ideas in the margins. Fill in the date and the name of the group at the top of the leader's page.

4 **Remove the TalkSheet from the book.** The pages are perforated along the left margin, for easy removal. Carefully tear out the TalkSheet you have chosen, thereby making it easier to copy. Before you run off copies, you might wish to "white out" (with liquid paper) the page number at the bottom of the TalkSheet.

5 **Make a copy for everyone in the group.** Each student will need their own copy of the TalkSheet. This book makes the assumption that everyone has access to a copy machine. Today's plain paper copiers make excellent copies and, in most cases, are inexpensive and easy to operate. Many churches have replaced their mimeograph machines with plain paper copiers. Any other method of printing or duplicating can be used, of course.

Obviously, you will make copies of only the student's side of the TalkSheet. The leader's material on the reverse side is just for you, the leader.

Keep in mind you are able to make copies for your group because we have given you permission to do so. U.S. copyright laws have not changed and it is still mandatory to request permission from a publisher before making copies of other published material. It is against the law not to do so. However, permission is given for you to make copies of *this* material for your **own group only,** not for every youth group in your state. Thank you for cooperating.

6 **Introduce the topic.** In most cases, it is important to introduce, or "set up", the topic before you pass out the TalkSheets to your group. Any method will suffice, as long as it is relatively short and to the point. Be careful not to "overintroduce" the topic. Be careful not to use an introduction that is "too preachy" or which resolves the issue before you even get started. You want to whet the appetites of the young people — to stretch their minds — and leave plenty of room for discussion. The primary purpose of the introduction is to spark interest in the topic.

The simplest way to introduce the topic is to do so verbally. You can tell a story, share an experience, or describe a situation or problem having to do with the topic. You might wish to evoke responses by asking a simple question, such as "What is the first thing you think of when you hear the word '_____' (the topic)?" After a few answers have been volunteered, you can reply, "It seems we all have different ideas about this subject. Tonight we're going to investigate it a bit further. . ." Then pass out the TalkSheet, make certain everyone has a pencil or pen, and you're on your way.

The following are excellent methods you can use to introduce any topic in this book:

1. Show a pertinent short film or video.
2. Read a passage from a book or magazine that relates to the subject.
3. Play a popular record that deals with the topic.
4. Perform a short skit or dramatic presentation.
5. Play a simulation game or "role play", setting up the topic.
6. Present current statistics, survey results, or read a current newspaper article which provides recent information about the topic.
7. Use a crowd breaker or game, getting into the topic in a humorous way. For example,

if the topic is "Fun", play a game to begin the discussion. If the topic is "Success", consider a game that helps the students experience success or failure.

8. Use posters, slides, or any other audio-visual aids to help focus attention on the topic.

There are endless possibilities. How you introduce the topic is entirely up to you. You are limited only by your own creativity. Each TalkSheet offers a few suggestions, but you are free to use any method with which you feel most comfortable. Keep in mind that the introduction is a very important part of each session. It will help set the tone and will influence the kinds of responses you get from the students. Don't "load" the introduction to the point that the group knows the "answer", or resolution, in advance or the students will not feel free to share their opinions openly and honestly.

Give your students enough time to work on their TalkSheet. Pass out a copy of the TalkSheet to each member of the group after the introduction. Each person should also have a pen or pencil and a Bible. There are usually five or six activities on each TalkSheet. If your time is limited, or if you are using only a portion of the TalkSheet to supplement your curriculum, instruct the group to complete only the activities you feel appropriate.

Decide ahead of time whether or not you wish the students to work on their TalkSheets individually or in groups.

Encourage them to consider what the Bible has to say about each topic as they complete the TalkSheets.

Give a time limit for completing the TalkSheet, and then when there is only a minute or two left to go, let them know. If the majority needs more time, allow it, if at all convenient. If most of the students have finished before the time is up, call "time" and begin the discussion.

Lead the discussion. The next step is to discuss the TalkSheet with the group. If you want to use these worksheets successfully, all members of your youth group should be encouraged to participate. It is important to foster an atmosphere conducive to discussion by communicating to the students the importance of each person's opinion. It is essential they understand their responsibility to contribute to the discussion. In order for these worksheets to have any meaning, there must be a variety of opinions.

If your youth group is very large, you may wish to divide it into smaller groups of 6 to 12. Each of these smaller groups should have a facilitator to keep the discussion going. The facilitator can be either an adult leader or a student member. Advise the leaders that they should be on an equal footing with the other members of the group. They should not try to dominate the others, and if the group looks to the facilitator for the "answer", ask the facilitator to direct the questions or responses back to the group. Once the smaller groups have completed their discussions, combine them into one large group and go through each of the items again, asking the different groups to summarize what they learned from each activity.

It is not necessary to divide into smaller groups every time you use the TalkSheets. Vary the groups, sometimes utilizing only large group discussion; other times, use smaller groups. You may wish, with certain subjects, to divide the meeting into groups of the same sex.

The discussion should concentrate on the questions and answers on the TalkSheet. Go through them one at a time, asking the students to share their responses to each item. Have them compare their answers and brainstorm new ones in addition to the ones they have written down. Those who don't feel comfortable revealing their answers should be allowed to pass on any question.

Don't feel pressured to spend time on every single activity. If time does not permit a discussion of every item, skip those that have evoked the least interest. Focus on those that appear to be the most stimulating to the whole group.

Follow your own creative instinct. If you discover a different way to use the activity, do so. Don't feel bound by the leader's instructions on the back of the TalkSheet. Use scriptures other than those designated. Add any items you feel pertinent. TalkSheets were designed to be open-ended in order for you to be able to add your own thoughts and ideas.

If the group begins digressing into an issue that has nothing to do with the main topic, guide them back on track. If, however, there is a high degree of interest in this "side issue", or if discussing it seems to meet a need of the majority, then you may wish to go ahead and see where the discussion leads. The point is to be as creative and flexible as necessary.

More information on leading discussions can be found in the next section.

9 **Wrap up the discussion.** This is your chance to present a challenge to the group. When considering your closing remarks, ask yourself the following question: "What do I want the students to remember most from this discussion?" If you can answer in two or three sentences, you have your closing remarks. It is important to bring some sort of conclusion to the session without negating the thoughts and opinions expressed by the students. A good wrap-up should affirm the group and offer a summary that helps tie the discussion together. Your students should be left with a desire to discuss the issue further or talk about it with a leader. Tell your group members you are available for private discussion after the session. In some cases, a wrap-up may be unnecessary. It might be more intriguing to leave the issue hanging and discuss it again at some later date. This will permit your students to think about it longer, on their own, and at a later date the loose ends can be tied down.

10 **Follow-up with an additional activity.** The leader's instructions on the back of the TalkSheet provide ideas for additional activities. They are optional but highly recommended. The purpose of these activities is to give the group the opportunity to reflect upon, evaluate, review, and assimilate what they have learned. Most of your TalkSheet discussions will only whet your students' appetites for further discussion on the subject. These additional activities will lead to more discussion and better learning.

Assign the activity and then follow-up with a short debriefing discussion at the next group meeting. The following are good questions to ask about the activity:

1. What happened when you did this activity? Was it helpful or a waste of time?
2. How did you feel when you were performing this activity?
3. Did the activity change your mind, or affect you in any way?
4. In one sentence, state what you learned from this activity.

HOW TO LEAD A TALKSHEET DISCUSSION

The young people of today are growing up in a world of moral confusion. The problem facing youth leaders is not so much teaching the church's beliefs and values as much as it is helping young people make the right choices in a world of so many options. Traditionally, the church's response to this problem has been to indoctrinate — to preach and yell its point of view louder than the rest of the world. Such an approach, however, does not work in today's world. Teenagers are hearing a variety of voices and messages, most of which are louder than those they are hearing from the church.

A TalkSheet discussion works for this very reason. While discussing the questions and activities on the TalkSheet, your youth group will be encouraged to think carefully about issues, to compare their beliefs and values with others, and to make discerning choices. TalkSheets will challenge your group to evaluate, defend, explain, and rework their ideas in an Christian atmosphere of acceptance, support, and growth.

CHARACTERISTICS OF A TALKSHEET DISCUSSION

Fruitful discussions — those that produce learning and growth — rarely happen by accident. A successful discussion requires careful preparation and a sensitive leader. Don't be concerned if you think you lack experience or don't have the time to spend lengthy hours in preparation. TalkSheets are designed to help even the novice leader conduct a memorable discussion. The more TalkSheet discussions you lead, the easier it will become. The following information should be extremely helpful. The ideas can be easily incorporated into your TalkSheet discussions.

Create a climate of acceptance. Most teenagers are afraid to express their opinions because they fear being ridiculed, laughed at and being considered "dumb" by their peers. They need to feel secure before they share their true feelings and beliefs. They also need to know they can share their thoughts and ideas, even if those are unpopular or "wild". If any of your group members are made to suffer put-downs, criticism, derisive laughter, or judgmental comments — even if their statements are opposed to the teachings of the Bible — an effective discussion cannot be accomplished.

For this reason each TalkSheet begins with a question or activity that is less threatening and more fun than some of those that follow. The first question helps the students become more comfortable with each other and with the prospect of sharing their ideas.

In order to help you transmit the idea of total acceptance, always phrase your questions — even those that are printed on the TalkSheets — in such a way that you are asking for an *opinion*, not an *answer*. For example, if a question reads, "What should Bill have done in that situation?", change it to "What **do you think** Bill should have done in that situation?" The simple addition of the three words "do you think" makes the question less threatening and a matter of opinion, rather than a demand for the "right" answer. When young people realize only their opinions are required, they will feel more comfortable and confident. In addition, the idea that a leader actually cares about their opinion on a subject boosts their self-image.

Affirm all legitimate expressions of opinion from your group members. Make certain everyone knows their comments and contributions are appreciated and important. This is especially true for those who rarely speak up in group activities. When they do, make a point of thanking them for joining in. This will be an incentive for them to participate further.

Remember affirmation does not always have to mean approval. Affirm even those comments that seem like "heresy" to you. By doing so, you inform the group that everyone has the right to express their ideas, no matter how controversial those ideas may be. If someone does express an opinion you believe is "way off base", make a mental note of the comment. Then, in your concluding remarks, refute the incorrect comment or present an alternative point of view, in a positive way. Do not reprimand the student who voiced the comment.

Discourage the students from thinking of you as the "authority" on the subject. It is typical of students to think you have the "right answer" to every question. They will look to you for approval, even when they are answering another group member's question. If you notice the responses focused primarily on you for this reason, redirect them toward the group by making a comment such as, "Talk to the group, not to me," or "Tell everyone, not just me."

Try to keep your purpose as "facilitator" as strong an image as possible. It is essential your students regard you as a member of the group, on an equal footing with them, whose primary aim is to keep the discussion alive and kicking. You are not sitting in judgment of their responses, nor do you have the correct answer for everything.

Remember, the less of an authority figure you appear to be, the more weight your own opinions will have to your impressionable teenagers. If you are regarded as a friend, they will give more credence to your words. You have a tremendous responsibility to be, with sincerity, their trusted friend.

Actively listen to each person. God gave you one mouth and two ears. Good discussion leaders know how to listen. Your job is not to monopolize the discussion, or to put in your two-cents worth on each issue. Keep your own mouth shut except when it encourages others to talk. Remember, you are a facilitator. You can express your opinions during your concluding remarks.

Do not force anyone to talk. Invite them, but do not insist they comment. Each member should have the right to "pass".

Do not take sides during the discussion. You will possibly have differing opinions in the group, from time to time. This is very stimulating to a discussion, but do not make the mistake of agreeing with one side or the other. Instead, encourage both sides to think through their positions and to defend their points of view. You may ask probing questions to encourage deeper examination of their opinions. If everyone seems to agree on a question, or if they seem reticent about expressing a controversial opinion, it might be wise to take the other side, playing the "devil's advocate" with tough questions, forcing them to stretch their thinking ability even more. Do not leave the impression the "other" point of view is necessarily your own. Remain neutral.

7 **Do not allow one person — including yourself — to monopolize the discussion.** Almost every group has "one person" who likes to talk and is perfectly willing to express an opinion on any subject. Try to encourage equal participation from all the students.

8 **Arrange seating to encourage discussion.** "Theater style" seating — in rows — is one of the worst ways to set up chairs for a discussion. If you must use chairs, arrange them in a circular or semi-circular pattern.

If the group is very large or if you notice the students are reluctant to participate, break them up into smaller groups of four or six per group. Have them discuss the questions and share their answers in the smaller group. This format is frequently less threatening to teenagers, especially if they represent a variety of maturity levels. If you have both junior high students and senior high students in the same youth meeting, let them divide up accordingly.

9 **Allow for humor when appropriate.** Do not take the discussions so seriously that they cannot be fun. Most TalkSheets include questions designed to generate laughter as well as intense, serious thought.

10 **Don't be intimidated by silence.** Silence is sometimes frightening to discussion leaders. Some react by trying to fill in the silence with a question or a comment. The following suggestions may help you handle silence more effectively:

a. Learn to feel comfortable with silence. Wait it out for 30 seconds. Give someone a reasonable time to respond. If you feel it appropriate, designate someone to comment. Sometimes a gentle nudge is all that is needed.

b. Discuss the silence with the group. Ask the students what the silence really means. Perhaps they are confused or embarrassed and don't feel free to share.

c. Answer the silence with questions or comments about it, such as "I know this is a difficult issue to consider. . ." or "It's scary to be the first to talk". Acknowledging the silence in this manner may break the ice.

d. Ask a different question that might be easier to handle, or that will clarify the one already posed. But do not do this too quickly. Wait, first.

11 **Try to keep the discussion under control.** It is common for a discussion to become sidetracked. You may not want the digression to continue.

If one of the group brings up a side issue that seems to generate a lot of interest and discussion, you will need to decide whether or not to pursue it or whether to redirect the disussion back to the original premise. If the interest is strong and the issue is worth discussion, sometimes the digression can be valuable. In most cases, however, it is advisable to say something like "Let's come back to that subject a little later if we have the time. Right now, let's finish our discussion on. . ."

12 **Be creative and flexible.** Do not feel pressured to follow the order of the questions on the TalkSheet. If you wish, use only a couple of them, or add a few of your own. The leader's guide on the back of the TalkSheet may give you some ideas, but think of your own as well. Each question or activity may lead to others along the same lines, which you can bring up during the discussion.

Be an "askable" discussion leader. Try to communicate to the students they can feel free to talk with you about anything, with confidentiality. Let them know you are there for them, with support and concern, even after the TalkSheet discussion has been completed.

 Know what your goals are. A TalkSheet discussion should be more than a "bull session". TalkSheets are designed to move along toward a goal, but you need to identify that goal in advance. What would you like your young people to learn? What truth should they discover? What is the goal of the session? If you don't know where you are going, it is doubtful you will get there.

GROUND RULES FOR AN EFFECTIVE TALKSHEET DISCUSSION

It may be helpful to begin your TalkSheet discussion with a few ground rules. Keep the rules to a minimum, of course, but most of the time knowing what is expected of them will be appreciated by the students. The following are suggestions for ground rules:

1 **"What is said in this room stays in this room."** Confidentiality is vitally important if a healthy discussion is to occur. The only time it should be broken is when a student reveals he or she is going to harm themselves or another.

2 **"No put-downs."** Mutual respect is important. If someone disagrees with another's comment, they can raise their hand for permission to express their own opinion of the subject, but not of the other person. It is acceptable to attack ideas but not each other.

3 **"There is no such thing as a dumb question."** Your group members must feel free to ask questions at any time. The best way to learn is to seek answers.

4 **"No one is forced to talk."** Let everyone know they have the right to pass or remain silent on any question.

5 **"Only one person speaks at a time."** This is a good way to teach mutual respect. Each person's opinion is worthwhile and deserves to be heard.

If members of the group violate these rules during the discussion or engage in disruptive or negative behavior, it would be wise to stop and deal with the problem before continuing.

USING THE BIBLE WITH THE TALKSHEETS

Adults often begin discussions with young people assuming teenagers believe the Bible has authority over their lives. Adults either begin their discussions with scripture or quickly support their contentions with Bible verses. But today's adolescents do not necessarily begin with the same assumption. They often begin with their own life situations, then decide if the Bible fits their needs. TalkSheets have been designed to begin your discussion with the realities of the adolescent world and then move toward scripture. This gives you the opportunity to show the Bible can be their guide and God does have something to say to them befitting their own unique situations.

The last activity on each TalkSheet involves scripture. These Bible references were selected for their relevance to each particular issue and for their potential to generate healthy discussion. They are not to be considered exhaustive. It has been assumed you will feel free to add whatever other scriptures you think pertinent. The passages listed are just the tip of the iceberg, inviting you to "search the scriptures" and dig deeper.

After the scriptures have been read aloud, ask your students to develop a Biblical principle that can guide their lives. For example, after reading the passages on the topic of Fun ("Kids Just Want to Have Fun"), the group may summarize by saying, "God wants us to have fun that is not harmful to us. It is best to include God in all of the fun we have."

A WORD OF CAUTION...

Many of the TalkSheets in this book deal with topics that may be sensitive or considered controversial. Discussing issues such as sexuality or even materialism may not be appreciated or understood by everyone in the church. Whenever you encourage discussion on such subjects, or invite your students to express their opinions (on any subject) no matter how "off base" they may be, you risk the possibility of being criticized by parents or other concerned people in your church. They may believe you are teaching heresy or questionable values.

The best way to avoid problems is to use good judgment. If you suspect a particular TalkSheet is going to cause problems, it would be expedient to think twice before you use it. Sometimes the damage done by proceeding against your better judgment outweighs the potential good you might achieve.

In order to avoid misunderstandings, provide parents and others to whom you might be accountable with copies of the TalkSheet before you use it. Inform them of the type of discussion you hope to encourage and the goal you hope to accomplish.

It is always a good idea for your students to take their TalkSheet home and discuss it with their parents. They might wish to ask their parents how they, as young people, would have answered some of the questions.

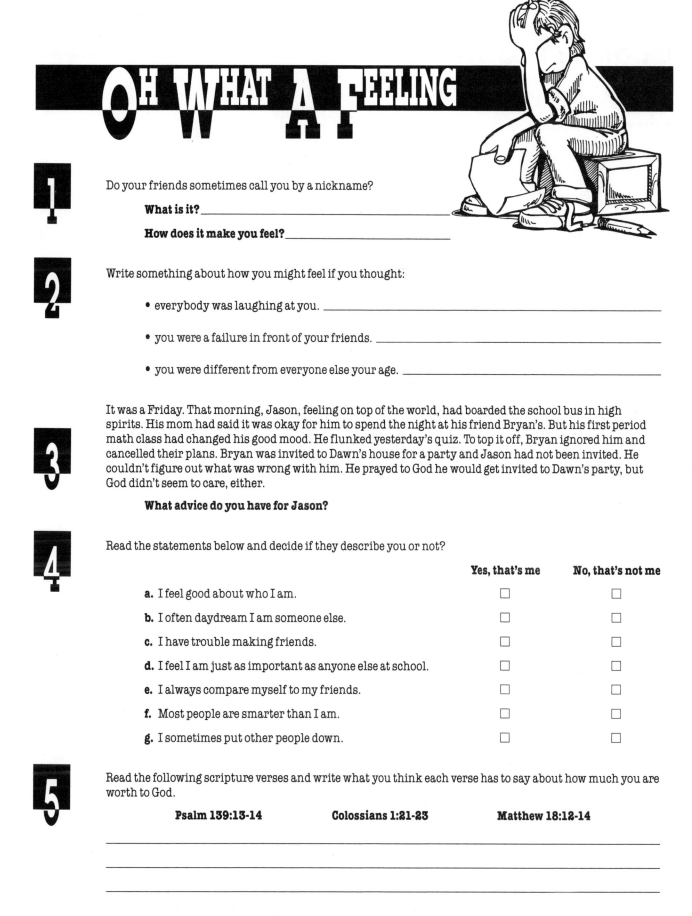

Oh What A Feeling

1 Do your friends sometimes call you by a nickname?

What is it? _____

How does it make you feel? _____

2 Write something about how you might feel if you thought:

• everybody was laughing at you. _____

• you were a failure in front of your friends. _____

• you were different from everyone else your age. _____

3 It was a Friday. That morning, Jason, feeling on top of the world, had boarded the school bus in high spirits. His mom had said it was okay for him to spend the night at his friend Bryan's. But his first period math class had changed his good mood. He flunked yesterday's quiz. To top it off, Bryan ignored him and cancelled their plans. Bryan was invited to Dawn's house for a party and Jason had not been invited. He couldn't figure out what was wrong with him. He prayed to God he would get invited to Dawn's party, but God didn't seem to care, either.

What advice do you have for Jason?

4 Read the statements below and decide if they describe you or not?

	Yes, that's me	No, that's not me
a. I feel good about who I am.	☐	☐
b. I often daydream I am someone else.	☐	☐
c. I have trouble making friends.	☐	☐
d. I feel I am just as important as anyone else at school.	☐	☐
e. I always compare myself to my friends.	☐	☐
f. Most people are smarter than I am.	☐	☐
g. I sometimes put other people down.	☐	☐

5 Read the following scripture verses and write what you think each verse has to say about how much you are worth to God.

Psalm 139:13-14   **Colossians 1:21-23**   **Matthew 18:12-14**

_____

_____

_____

Date Used: _____

Group: _____

OH, WHAT A FEELING

Topic: Feelings of Inferiority.

Purpose of this Session:

It is common for all of us, occasionally, to have feelings of inferiority. During the junior high years, these feelings are intensified. Many of us have all but forgotten our own young feelings of inferiority because they were so painful. This session examines those feelings of rejection, hurt and inferiority and gives you the opportunity to talk about these feelings in a warm, supportive Christian environment.

To Introduce the Topic:

When discussing inferiority, it is imperative the students feel secure enough to talk. That means no put-downs. As leader, your responsibility is to insure the students do not ridicule each other. Introduce this session with a community building game which will decrease put-downs and promote a positive environment.

The "Gratitude Game" is excellent for this purpose. Ask a member of the group to come to the front or sit in a special chair. Then ask the rest to brainstorm what things they would be thankful for, if they were the person selected. This can be very affirmative and a lot of fun. Try it with several students, or all of them, if time allows.

The Discussion:

Item #1: The purpose of this item is to allow the students to reflect on their emotions concerning the nicknames others have given them. Begin by sharing a nickname you had as a teen and how you felt about it. Then ask if the students would be willing to share their nicknames and their feelings about them. It isn't necessary to spend a lot of time on this item, however, and never force anyone to share an embarrassing nickname.

You may wish to illustrate how nicknames which are actually put-downs, such as "Fatso" and "Board", can hurt and should not be used. We cannot look good when we put others down. We should not lower ourselves by demeaning others.

Item #2: Make certain the students have an opportunity to share their feelings without being afraid everyone will laugh at them. You might share some of your own junior high experiences. Don't force participation from anyone who appears to be reticent.

Ask the young people to share some positive times, as well. Times when they felt really great, when people applauded them or when they felt successful, proud, and accepted by others.

Item #3: This "Tension Getter" allows the students to play counselor and give advice to someone else about feelings of inadequacy. Brainstorm with the students several choices Jason could make. Then illustrate how these ideas could apply to their own situations.

Item #4: Choose two or three of the less threatening statements and ask for a show of hands to find out who checked "Yes, that's me" or "No, that's not me". Some will not want to share their answers. Keep in mind there are no right nor wrong answers here. Discuss each one without being too dogmatic. Focus more on how the students feel. During the closure time, you might choose to go back and refer to some of the statements in a more instructive way. It may be tempting to tell the students how they should feel, but it is better to simply listen and show them you care and want to understand what is going on in their changing bodies and minds.

Item #5: The scriptures listed here give you an opportunity to focus the discussion on God's unconditional love and acceptance for us. You can guide the discussion toward God's feeling for us. Psalm 139:13-14 is a very positive scripture upon which to focus your attention. Listen carefully to the students as they give their paraphrases of the scriptures.

To Close the Session:

Help the students understand feelings are neither good nor bad. They are just there. Sometimes we imply certain feelings are sinful. Teenagers need to understand it is not the feeling but what is done with the feeling that makes the difference. When they feel down about themselves, they need to be careful not to do something they will regret later. Feelings are temporary and will go away. But the consequences of sinful behavior will cause problems for a long time.

Emphasize that each of the students is a special, gifted person created in the image of God Himself. While there are times when all of us feel inferior and disappointed in ourselves, we should never lose sight of the fact that God thinks we are terrific. He is our biggest fan. "If God has a wallet, our picture is in it!"

It is important to let the group know feelings of inferiority are normal and experienced by everyone their age and older. Even people who seem to be confident and who have everything a person could ever want feel insecure at times. Challenge your students to accept God's love and forgiveness, even when they don't feel loved or forgiven.

Outside Activities:

1. Ask each person to think of himself or herself as a place and to draw a map which will describe that place. For example, what would you look like if you were a city, or an island in the middle of an ocean? What kinds of buildings, hills, valleys, roads (some under construction), areas of interest, etc., would be there?

2. Ask the students to bring a favorite record, tape or video to share that best expresses how they feel. Play the music and discuss why it describes their emotion.

3. Have the members of the group keep a journal of feelings for a week, writing down the feelings they have during each day.

FOOTLOOSE

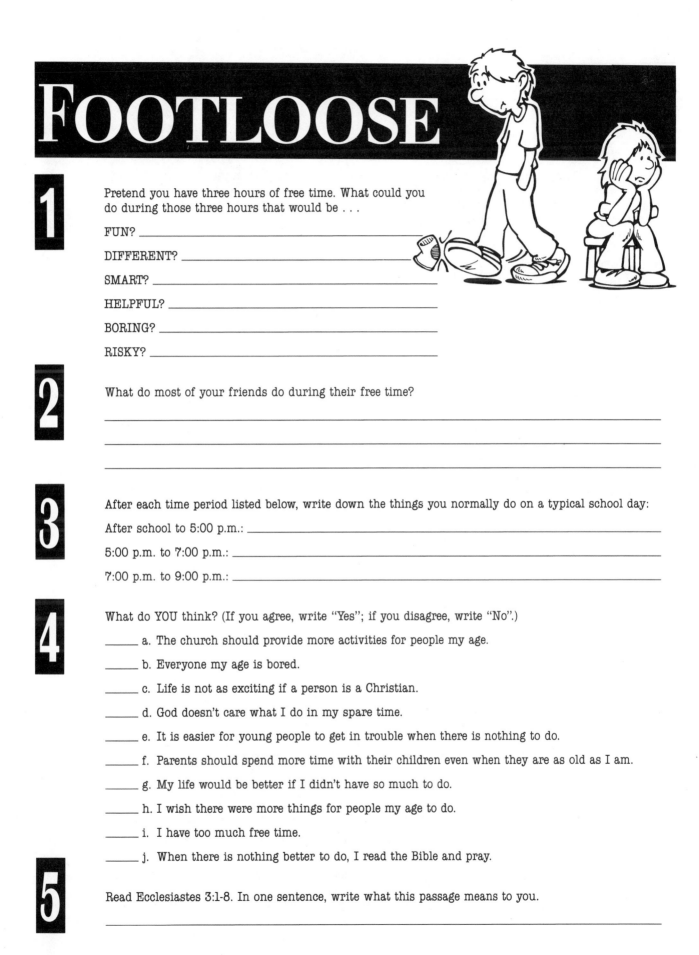

1 Pretend you have three hours of free time. What could you do during those three hours that would be . . .

FUN? _____

DIFFERENT? _____

SMART? _____

HELPFUL? _____

BORING? _____

RISKY? _____

2 What do most of your friends do during their free time?

_____

_____

_____

3 After each time period listed below, write down the things you normally do on a typical school day:

After school to 5:00 p.m.: _____

5:00 p.m. to 7:00 p.m.: _____

7:00 p.m. to 9:00 p.m.: _____

4 What do YOU think? (If you agree, write "Yes"; if you disagree, write "No".)

_____ a. The church should provide more activities for people my age.

_____ b. Everyone my age is bored.

_____ c. Life is not as exciting if a person is a Christian.

_____ d. God doesn't care what I do in my spare time.

_____ e. It is easier for young people to get in trouble when there is nothing to do.

_____ f. Parents should spend more time with their children even when they are as old as I am.

_____ g. My life would be better if I didn't have so much to do.

_____ h. I wish there were more things for people my age to do.

_____ i. I have too much free time.

_____ j. When there is nothing better to do, I read the Bible and pray.

5 Read Ecclesiastes 3:1-8. In one sentence, write what this passage means to you.

_____

FOOTLOOSE

Topic: Free Time

Purpose of this Session:

During the junior high years, young people have more freedom and mobility than they have ever had before. The term "latchkey kids" has been coined to refer to the growing number of young people who come home from school to empty houses. The many hours of unsupervised time today's youngsters have gives them more freedom to experiment with new behaviors and identities. This session allows you to discuss how Christians can handle free time.

To Introduce the Topic:

Pass out pencils and paper and have the group complete the sentence, "When I have free time, I usually. . .". Ask them to sign the papers and collect them. Tell them not to let anyone see their answers. Then ask them to guess how others might have completed the sentence. This can be lots of fun and can provide a smooth transition into the topic of free time.

The Discussion:

Item #1: Ask the students to share their responses. Encourage creative thinking and ask for as many ideas as possible. List them on a sheet of newsprint or on the blackboard.

Item #2: List the items, then have the students rate them as to their "goodness" or "badness" (10 can be good, 1 can be bad). Or choose the best five and the worst five. It is important the students understand they have a great many choices when it comes to using free time — some good and some bad.

Item #3: This item gives the students a chance to look at how they spend a typical school day. You might wish to do the same exercise using a week-end. Focus on the fact that everyone has the same length of time, every day, but each chooses to use it differently. For those who state they are bored, have nothing to do, etc., you might wish to suggest ways in which they can best use their time. Ask the students to offer ideas and help each other.

Item #4: This item should stimulate a lot of discussion. Go over each of the statements, asking for opinions. Try to direct the discussion toward constructive decisions and actions. If the students agree with the statement, "The church should provide more activities for people my age", discuss what can be done and how they as a group can take some responsibility for achieving the desired result.

Item #5: This passage of scripture demonstrates the balance necessary in our use of time. Ask the group to share their sentences. Go through the passage and ask them to give modern-day examples of each of the activities mentioned in the verses.

To Close the Session:

Challenge the students as Christians to make wise use of their precious time. Time is a gift from God and should not be wasted. Encourage them to take time to do constructive things that will help them grow as a person — like reading books or visiting a museum. Encourage them to take time to relax — to do nothing or to take a nap occasionally. Stress that it is vitally important for them to have fun but to do it in a positive manner. You might wish to brainstorm with the group ways in which they can have a good time, earn money, or can help others, etc. Challenge them to use part of their free time for devotions and service to God.

Outside Activities:

1. Have the students vote on a service project they can do together after school or on a weekend, such as visiting a rest home, collecting food for a food bank, performing yard work for the elderly, etc.

2. Ask them to keep a log of their daily activities for a week or a weekend to find out how they spend their time. Discuss what they learned about themselves from the log.

3. Help those who are interested find part-time, after-school jobs that will enable them to earn money. You might wish to set up a "job bank", in which you match up students with jobs people in the church need done, such as housework, mowing lawns, washing cars, sweeping sidewalks, taking inventory, etc.

GREAT EXPECTATIONS

1 Write a word you think best describes the teenage years.

_____

2 What one thing worries you the most about becoming a teenager?

_____

_____

3 On the space provided, write what you would tell someone your age who. . .

a...was having trouble making friends.

_____

b...could not get along with his or her parents.

_____

c...did not like the way he or she looked.

_____

d...was trying to act "older" than he or she really is.

_____

4 Write a "G" next to the following which sound like "good news" and a "B" next to those that sound like "bad news".

_____ classes in high school

_____ driving a car

_____ learning about sex

_____ getting a job

_____ more freedom from parents

_____ dating

_____ temptations, such as drugs or alcohol

_____ youth group

_____ making your own decisions

_____ making new friends

_____ planning a career

_____ buying your own clothes

5 Read the following verses and summarize them in five words or less.

Psalm 119:9-11 _____

I Timothy 4:12 _____

Titus 2:6-8 _____

Date Used: _____

Group: _____

GREAT EXPECTATIONS

Topic: Preparing for the adolescent years.

Purpose of the Session:

Today our children are growing up in a world full of rapid change, confusion and stress. When these are added to the normal changes that take place during adolescence (physical, intellectual, etc.) many young people find it more than difficult to cope. Not enough time is spent helping our children make the difficult transition into the adolescent years. This session is designed to let the youngsters know it is permissable to talk about the issues they will face as they grow older. It encourages them to ask questions and share their worries and fears. This TalkSheet would be excellent to use with pre-teens (ages 10-12), as well as junior high students.

To Introduce the Topic:

A good way to introduce this topic is to have your group suggest movies or a television shows about teenagers. Make a list of their choices and ask the students to decide whether or not these programs or films are "telling the truth" about teenagers or are "not realistic".

Another introduction would be to present the group with a selection of teenage magazines and conduct a "magazine scavenger hunt". Divide the group into teams, each team receiving a magazine. The leader then calls out the name of something commonly advertised (such as "Milky Way"), an often-used word (such as "totally"), a teen idol (such as "Madonna"), a movie title (such as "Rambo"), etc. Each team tries to find the item as quickly as possible in their magazine. The first team to do so wins.

The Discussion:

Item #1: List all the words written describing the students' idea of the teen years. Take plenty of time talking about each one. Focus on what your students are feeling — their fears, excitement, anxiety. They have probably heard all kinds of myths about being a teenager. Some of these misconceptions will be obvious from the words they have chosen. Most of these erroneous ideas focus on adult-type behaviors. They might be convinced they will have to drink alcohol, engage in illicit sex, party wildly, etc. Try to dispel these assumptions. This discussion can help your teens have a healthier, more realistic expectation of adolescence.

Item #2: Most students will be too embarrassed to share their answer to this question. You may wish to ask, "What do you think worries other kids your age about becoming a teenager?" They will feel more at ease talking about an hypothetical "other" than about themselves. Write down their responses on the blackboard and assure them that all these worries are perfectly normal. Everyone worries about new experiences and they will be having a lot of new ones as they enter their teen years. Most of the time, these worries about the "unknown" go away as soon as it becomes a "known". Situations are never as bad as we can imagine them to be.

Item #3: Ask the students to reveal their answers to each of these situations. Ask if they agree or disagree with the advice given. Stress how important it is for them to support and encourage each other. So many teens and pre-teens put each other down. As Christians, they have a responsibility to minister to and help their peers.

Item #4: This item gives you a chance to talk about what your students can expect in high school. Try to keep the discussion upbeat and end on a positive note. Some children are really worried about being a teenager. Ease their anxiety by letting them see all of the items can be "good news" if they respond to them appropriately. Let them know you are available to help them deal with all of these things and to offer advice or answer any questions they might have.

Item #5: Encourage several of the students to read their summaries aloud. Get them to draw out applications for their world from these summaries. An appropriate scripture to concentrate on is I Timothy 4:12.

To Close this Session:

Emphasize the fact that the early adolescent years are both the best and the most confusing years of the students' entire lives. Assure them they are perfectly normal and stress the fact that God intended for their lives to be full of change and growth during these years. A good comparison is the caterpillar, who at a certain time of its life cycle goes into a cocoon, emerging later as a beautiful butterfly. In the same way, as the teenage years approach, everyone changes — in different ways and at different speeds — into the person that God wants them to be.

Outside Activities:

1. Have the members of your group tape interviews with several high school students, asking them what it is like to be in high school, how difficult it is to be a Christian in high school, how to get along with parents, etc. Ask them to write out their list of questions beforehand. Debrief the interviews later, after playing them for the whole group. You may wish to preview the tapes.

2. Construct a "Dear Gabby" box in which the students can drop their questions about adolescence. Use a shoe box with a slit cut in the top. Put 3x5 cards and pencils near the box or pass them out at the end of the meeting. Answer the questions the following week or give them to the students to answer. If you decide to give them out to the group, keep them anonymous.

3. Have the students tape interviews with elderly persons, asking them what it was like when they were teenagers. The students should write their own questions. Play the interviews and discuss what was learned.

SCHOOL DAZE

1 What is your favorite class in school?

_____

Why is it your favorite? _____

_____

Who is your favorite teacher? _____

Why is he or she your favorite? _____

_____

2 Place an X on the line below indicating how you feel about your relationship to God when you are at school.

_____

Close to God   **Far from God**

3 What do you think?

	Agree	Disagree	Don't Know
a. If you don't get good grades, then you are a failure.	☐	☐	☐
b. I have no Christian friends in school.	☐	☐	☐
c. A person should not be required to go to school.	☐	☐	☐
d. I feel out of place in my school.	☐	☐	☐
e. People at school really care about me and my feelings.	☐	☐	☐
f. What I learn at church helps me in school.	☐	☐	☐
g. I wish I could go to another school.	☐	☐	☐
h. People at school don't understand my Christian beliefs.	☐	☐	☐
i. Most of my classes are a waste of time.	☐	☐	☐
j. My school is really fun.	☐	☐	☐

5

4 Read Proverbs 9:10. In one sentence, write what you think it means.

_____

_____

_____

_____

Date Used: _____

Group: _____

SCHOOL DAZE

Topic: School

Purpose of this Session:

Junior high students spend a large part of their time in school. Some enjoy it, while others hate it. Most fall somewhere in between. Christian students need a chance to talk about their concerns and frustrations with school. This TalkSheet gives you a chance to listen to them and to encourage their comments about school.

To Introduce the Topic:

Write the following incomplete sentence on a chalkboard, an overhead projector, or a large sheet of newsprint: "My school is a place where. . .". Ask the students to complete the sentence. This will get the group talking about their schools. Another good partial sentence to use is "If I were the principal of my school, I would. . .".

Another way is to begin the session with a pop quiz. Run the test like a school teacher, with no talking, no looking at others' papers, etc. The quiz could cover a book of the Bible or whatever was discussed the week before. The students will probably complain that this activity is "just like school". Once the short test is over, move on to the "School Daze" TalkSheet.

The Discussion:

Item #1: This focuses on the positive. Allow the students to share their answers. Find out why they chose the classes they did for their favorites. The second part of the question gives them a chance to talk about what they like about their favorite teachers. You may learn something new about what teenagers want to see in adult leaders. Make a list of all the positive characteristics mentioned.

Item #2: Many young students have difficulty relating their Christian faith to their school. Let them share how difficult it can be sometimes to be a Christian at school. Those who attend Christian schools may have even more frustrations. They are often angry and resent having to attend a Christian school as well as church. Let them feel free to vent these frustrations.

Item #3: Spend some time discussing the first statement concerning grades. Help the students realize that even though there is a lot of pressure on them to get good marks, grades are not necessarily indicative of intelligence or success in life. There are many famous and brilliant people who never did well in school. Encourage them to try always to do their best and let the grades take care of themselves.

Items b, f, and h give you an additional chance to discuss your group's Christian faith while in school. If this area has already been talked over, move on to the other statements. The other items deal with their feelings about fitting in at school. Many children at the junior high level have feelings of inferiority, especially in relation to school. They need to articulate these feelings while away from the school environment.

Item #4: Ask the students to apply this verse to education. Emphasize the "fear of God" does not mean "being afraid of God". The "fear of God" is better defined as "having a close relationship with Him".

To Close the Session:

Help your group members understand that school is an important time of preparation for them. They not only learn what is taught in their classes, but they also learn the discipline of going there on a daily basis. They learn self-respect and a sense of identity by following through on assignments, by working hard on projects, by experimentation, and by interacting with their peers and adult leaders. God will work through the teachers and school officials to help make them better people and better equipped to be successful in the real world.

Challenge them to take their faith to school with them. They need to know their Christianity is far more than just Sunday at church. Is is also for Monday at school. Show empathy and understanding for the problems they face at school. Let them know you are available to listen. Encourage them to have Christian friends as well as non-Christian friends at school. It is important for them to have the support of other Christians at school.

Outside Activities:

1. Join your students at their school during lunch. Talk about how they feel about the teachers and fellow students, but use discretion. Teenagers are extremely self-conscious and easily embarrassed. It would be unwise if your discussion was overheard.

2. Have a social event with another church in your area. This way, your students can meet other Christians who attend their school.

3. Send each of your students a postcard this week that encourages them in their school work.

4. Have a Sunday afternoon study hall with "fun-breaks" the next time your group members have exams. Alternate games and healthy snacks with a quiet study period.

AM I NORMAL?

1 The best age to be is: (circle one)

2   5   10   13   16   18   21   30   45   65

2 Complete the following sentence with the answer that best suits you:

I am growing up . . .

    a. faster than most my age

    b. about the same as others my age

    c. slower than others my age

3 If you could change one thing about yourself, what would it be?

_____

_____

4 When I look in the mirror, I feel: (check only two)

_____ worried   _____ angry   _____ embarrassed   _____ special

_____ proud   _____ flawed   _____ lonely   _____ handsome

_____ happy   _____ shy   _____ pretty   _____ depressed

5 Check each of the following you believe are normal behaviors and concerns for a person your age.

_____ dating

_____ worrying about others' opinions of me

_____ how my hair looks

_____ grades

_____ nuclear war

_____ getting along with my parents

_____ what God thinks of me

_____ getting a good job

_____ how sexy I am

_____ getting accepted at a college

_____ how late I can stay out at night

_____ my body's appearance, as compared to others

_____ how to lose weight

_____ how to make new friends

_____ how to be a better Christian

6 Draw connecting lines between the scripture verses and the appropriate statements.

Luke 2:51-52	God was with her.
2 Timothy 3:15	Left his family and wanted his money
2 Chronicles 34:1-2	Knew scriptures even as a child
Luke 15:11-13	Jesus growing up
Luke 1:26-28	Did the right thing in God's eyes

Date Used: _____

Group: _____

AM I NORMAL?

Topic: Growing up

Purpose of this Session:

Growing up produces all kinds of conflicting emotions. Many young people feel they are somehow different from others and not progressing normally. This session has been designed to encourage talking about how it feels to be growing up. It also gives you, the leader, a chance to affirm your students and also to teach them to encourage and support each other.

To Introduce the Session:

Some advanced preparation with this is well worth the effort. Record on tape statements from some respected members of your adult congregation talking about their own experiences when they were junior high students. Word association is a good way to begin. A few key words are: puberty, parents, school, friends, looks, music, feelings, problems, homework, the opposite sex. Play the tape for your youth group and begin your discussion with these same subjects.

The Discussion:

Item #1: This presents a fun way to begin. Have the students vote on their choice of the "perfect age". Ask them to give their reasons for choosing this age. Point out that every age is unique unto itself and offers new and exciting experiences. Old age is not called "The Golden Age" without good reason.

Item #2: Emphasize the fact that everyone grows at a different pace. During early adolescence, it is "normal" for some to mature as much as six years earlier than others. Girls, particularly, will mature physically much younger than boys. Point out that it all evens out in a few years.

Item #3: Ease the tension that may exist with this item by beginning the discussion with changes that happened to you when you were in junior high school. Once the students have shared their own changes, explain that their feelings are normal. Nearly everyone wishes to make changes in themselves.

Item #4: This item opens up the discussion on the students' self-image. The responses will be good indicators of their self-esteem. You may want to share what your own self-image was as a teen and what Christ had done for you. You may also wish to collect their TalkSheets (unsigned) to read how all chose to answer this item.

Item #5: Young people at the junior high age level are particularly sensitive about fitting in, being normal, and going along with whatever their peers think best. Use this item to talk about what is "normal". Today's young person has far too many adult worries and responsibilities. They have literally lost some of their childhood. Ask them to arrange these concerns into two categories: those that need attention now and those that can wait until a later date in their lives. Then give your views about what is normal and healthy for their age. Mention realistic expectations of themselves and others.

Item #6: Each of these scriptures deals with growing up. You may wish to focus attention on Luke 2:51-52 and talk about Christ's childhood.

To Close the Session:

A comprehensive conclusion is to summarize the feelings and thoughts the students shared, showing them they are normal. It is important to stress God's understanding and love. God does know how painful it is to grow up because Jesus was once their age and really cares for them.

Outside Activities:

1. Ask the students to bring a record, a cassette or video to the youth group meeting that best describes how they feel about growing up. After previewing the material, play those you wish to discuss with the group.

2. Ask the students to keep a journal of their feelings and thoughts for a week. Discuss what it was like to write these down.

3. Have the students make a collage that best describes how they feel as young people. Ask them to bring their collages to the youth group and share them. Keep several to share with parents and church members.

All in the Family

1 Write down three activities your family does together:

a. _____

b. _____

c. _____

Circle the one you enjoy the most.

2 Circle three words from those below which best describe your family:

Fun	Busy	Happy	Embarrassing	Loving	Strange
Close	Christian	Changing	Critical	Peaceful	Strict
Boring	Stressful	Noisy	Friendly	Helpful	

3 If you could change one thing about your family, what would it be?

_____

_____

_____

4 Check any of the following you would like to learn more about:

_____ how to get along better with my brothers and sisters

_____ how to get my parents off my back

_____ how to have more fun as a family

_____ how to get along better with my parents

_____ how to have a "closer" family

_____ how to have family devotions

_____ how to tell my parents how I really feel

5 Read the following scripture verses and write down what you think each verse has to say about your family.

Proverbs 6:20-22 _____

Romans 12:9-13 _____

Ephesians 6:1-4 _____

_____

ALL IN THE FAMILY

Topic: Family Life

Purpose of this Session:

Junior high students are at an age where they are desperately trying to seek an identity of their own, apart from the family. This often results in frustration, tension and disharmony within the family group. This TalkSheet was designed to help your students better understand their family and will give them a chance to ask questions which can strengthen their family ties. It is important for you, the leader, to remember within our society there are a great many types of families. There are traditional families, divorced families, single-parent families, or families with foster children. Do not assume all your students live in a traditional two-parent environment.

To Introduce the Topic:

Ask the students to think of as many television play families as they can. Write them on the blackboard. Then ask which one they would like to be a member of, and why.

Perhaps it would be feasible to ask one of the senior citizens in the church talk about family life as it was 50 years ago and compare it with family life today. Your young people will probably be fascinated.

Before distributing this TalkSheet, be certain your students know their answers and comments will be kept confidential. If they think you might tell their parents or guardians their comments, they will be reluctant to answer candidly.

The Discussion:

Item #1: This emphasizes the positive experiences the students have had with their families. Ask them to share stories of their fun family times.

Item #2: Ask for a sharing of the words they chose to describe their families. If you wish to keep this on a positive note, ask how many chose words that were positive or good. Then you can ask how many chose words that were negative or bad. Rather than having the students share the negative words, you might wish to point out that all families are a mixture of both positive and negative characteristics. Sometimes it is easier to think of the negative than the the positive.

Ask for the students to volunteer other descriptive words about their families.

Item #3: Allow the students to share the changes they would like to see. Make a list of their suggestions on the blackboard. Cross off all those that are unrealistic (such as "Get rid of my two sisters"). With those that remain, brainstorm ways they can help achieve these changes.

Permit mild complaints about family situations, but close on a positive note. Young people need a chance to "let off steam" regarding their home life. However, you as a youth worker need to be supportive of family life. Keep a balance. Listen to the students' complaints without letting the discussion become a "gripe session" and remain supportive of their parents or guardians.

Item #4: This can be used as a checklist to generate future topics as well as a discussion topic itself. You may wish to collect the unsigned TalkSheets at the end of the session for future reference. Spend a few minutes brainstorming ways to learn more information about the topics checked.

Item #5: Ask for several volunteers to share their thoughts on these scriptures. Focus on one in particular. If you choose Ephesians 6:1-4, talk about the natural balance and reciprocal nature of the parent-child relationship. Then discuss how the students, as Christians, can do their part in improving the relationships they have at home.

To Close the Session:

Stress the fact that no family is perfect, because we as family members are not perfect as individuals. Parents are not perfect and neither are children. However, we can all improve if we are willing to make changes. The late President John F. Kennedy is famous for this statement: "Ask not what your country can do for you, but instead what you can do for your country." The same is true for families. If we want more love in our families, then we need to bring more love into them. It is not the parents' responsibility alone. There are many things young people can do to encourage harmony and happiness in their families. Are they willing to try?

Communicate your willingness to help those who are having very difficult problems at home. The young people in your group need to know you understand and are available to listen. Also communicate God's willingness to help them.

Outside Activities:

1. Have the students watch a television program involving a family, such as "The Cosby Show". Have them observe the type of family personified, the positive and negative aspects of the family, and how realistically the family is portrayed. It might be fun to let them pretend they are television critics who critique family sit-coms.

2. Have a family activity with your students and include their parents or guardians. Play games together, have fun together, then have the students discuss with their parents how they (the students) plan to help improve their home life.

Watch That Music

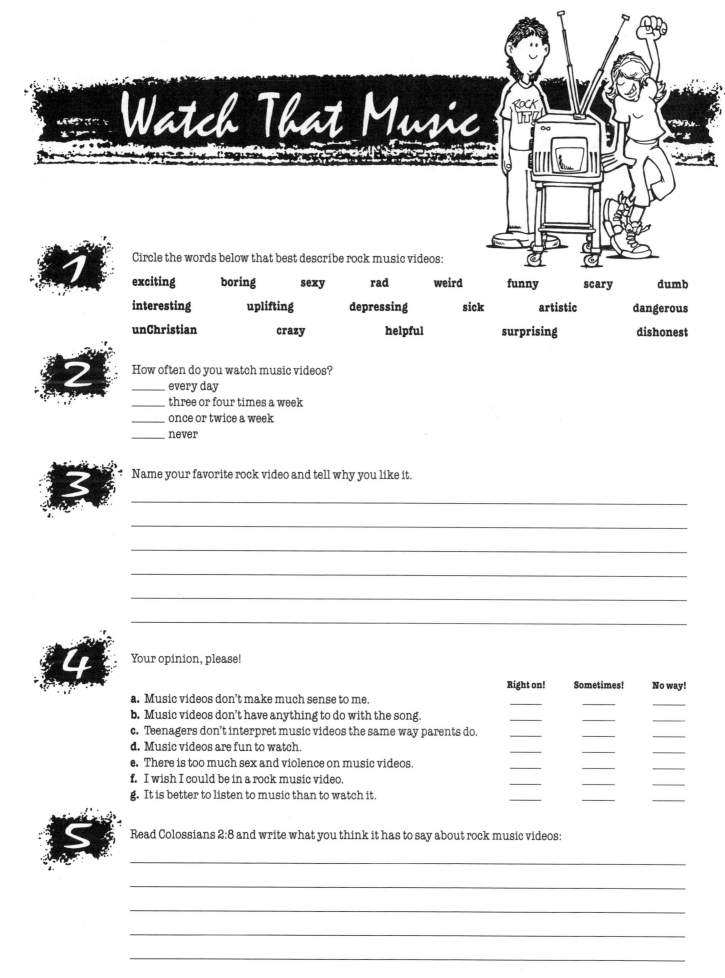

1 Circle the words below that best describe rock music videos:

exciting	boring	sexy	rad	weird	funny	scary	dumb
interesting	uplifting		depressing	sick	artistic		dangerous
unChristian	crazy		helpful		surprising		dishonest

2 How often do you watch music videos?
_____ every day
_____ three or four times a week
_____ once or twice a week
_____ never

3 Name your favorite rock video and tell why you like it.

_____

_____

_____

_____

_____

_____

4 Your opinion, please!

	Right on!	Sometimes!	No way!
a. Music videos don't make much sense to me.	_____	_____	_____
b. Music videos don't have anything to do with the song.	_____	_____	_____
c. Teenagers don't interpret music videos the same way parents do.	_____	_____	_____
d. Music videos are fun to watch.	_____	_____	_____
e. There is too much sex and violence on music videos.	_____	_____	_____
f. I wish I could be in a rock music video.	_____	_____	_____
g. It is better to listen to music than to watch it.	_____	_____	_____

5 Read Colossians 2:8 and write what you think it has to say about rock music videos:

_____

_____

_____

_____

_____

Date Used: _____

Group: _____

WATCH THAT MUSIC!

Topic: Rock music videos

Purpose of this Session:

Many of the members of your youth group are probably becoming rock video addicts. With the proliferation of rock videos and "music channels" in the last few years, it is important to discuss which videos they watch, how they are influenced by them, and how they can make decisions about them in the future.

To Introduce this Session:

If you have access to a video recorder, tape a popular music video and play it for the group meeting. A giant-screen television set would be ideal, as would a sound system that could amplify the music as loud as your students would like it. Use discretion when choosing a sample rock video, as some are not G-rated.

The Discussion:

Item #1: Ask the students to share the words chosen and explain why. Expect a wide variety of answers.

Item #2: Ask for a show of hands to find out who watches music videos the most and who watches the least. You might want to give a special "Vidiot Award" to the student who watches the most, just for fun.

Item #3: Ask the students to share the names of their favorite videos and to tell why they like them. Use this time to discuss how they can decide between a good and a bad video.

Item #4: Have the students take a stand — literally — corresponding to their votes. Have them take up positions under signs in the room marked "Right on!", "Sometimes!" and "No Way!". On statements that evoke a lot of differing opinions, have the students give reasons for their choices.

Item #5: Ask for volunteers to share their interpretations of this passage. Ask them whether they view rock videos as "worldly philosophy" or not.

To Close the Session:

Try to maintain a balanced perspective during your conclusion. Too many times we are inclined to summarize a session such as this in a negative way, which serves only to turn the young people away from what is being taught. The key issues here are (1) how to make a wise decision about which videos to watch, and (2) what is the best way to use valuable time. It is extemely important to discuss the influence rock music videos have on your students. Most of the time, we do not realize we are being influenced by things we see and hear.

Help your students understand rock music videos are like anything else in life we have to make wise decisions about. They are not neutral and the choice is ours. We must be concerned about what we put in our minds and bodies. Rock videos are not inherently bad, but if they are teaching us things that are contrary to the values of the Christian faith, then we must reject them.

The issue of "time" is a major one. Young people often spend many, many hours in front of the television set. Is this the best use of the time God has given us? Unlike music alone, videos require our total attention. There is also the question of creative imagination. Ask them if rock videos are replacing their gift of originality and imagination by controlling their own private interpretation of a song. Music videos are programmed to interpret a song for us. Is this good or bad?

There are now many outstanding Christian rock videos available for rent or for sale, which you might wish to show your youth group.

Outside Activities:

1. Suggest your students watch a rock music video with their parents and discuss it with them.

2. Have the group watch an hour of music videos together and rate them according to a set of criteria you have formulated with them. Do they support or tear down Christian values? Are the videos a good interpretation of the songs? Is illicit sex, violence, drug use, or negative behavior being promoted, glamourized or exploited?

DRINK, DRANK, DRUNK

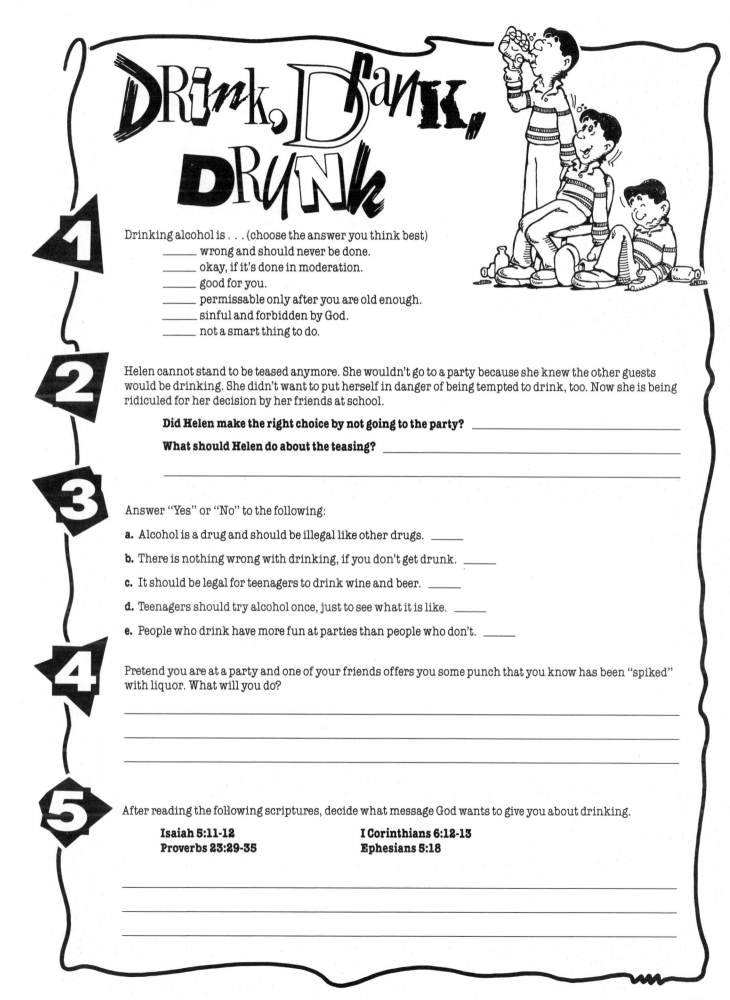

1 Drinking alcohol is . . . (choose the answer you think best)

_____ wrong and should never be done.

_____ okay, if it's done in moderation.

_____ good for you.

_____ permissable only after you are old enough.

_____ sinful and forbidden by God.

_____ not a smart thing to do.

2 Helen cannot stand to be teased anymore. She wouldn't go to a party because she knew the other guests would be drinking. She didn't want to put herself in danger of being tempted to drink, too. Now she is being ridiculed for her decision by her friends at school.

Did Helen make the right choice by not going to the party? _____

What should Helen do about the teasing? _____

_____

3 Answer "Yes" or "No" to the following:

a. Alcohol is a drug and should be illegal like other drugs. _____

b. There is nothing wrong with drinking, if you don't get drunk. _____

c. It should be legal for teenagers to drink wine and beer. _____

d. Teenagers should try alcohol once, just to see what it is like. _____

e. People who drink have more fun at parties than people who don't. _____

4 Pretend you are at a party and one of your friends offers you some punch that you know has been "spiked" with liquor. What will you do?

_____

_____

_____

5 After reading the following scriptures, decide what message God wants to give you about drinking.

Isaiah 5:11-12   **I Corinthians 6:12-13**
Proverbs 23:29-35   **Ephesians 5:18**

_____

_____

_____

27

Date Used: _____

Group: _____

DRINK, DRANK, DRUNK

Topic: Alcohol

Purpose of this Session:

Adolescents are drinking more than Kool-Aid and soft drinks these days. Children are consuming alcohol in alarming quantities, from wine-coolers to hard liquor. This TalkSheet provides you with a forum to discuss what a Christian young person should do about alcoholic beverages.

To Introduce the Session:

Begin by brainstorming with your group the reasons teenagers drink alcohol. List the reasons for all to see on newsprint or chalkboard. You can set the tone of the discussion here by listening carefully, with respect, to the opinions of each of the group members. If you can refrain from stating your opinions until later and listen to your students now, they will more likely listen to you later and respect your beliefs.

The Discussion:

Item #1: Ask for sharing on views about alcohol. If there are various opinions, let the students debate their answers by giving reasons for their views.

Item #2: This "Tension Getter" will help the students talk about the peer pressure concerning alcohol. Let the group consider different approaches Helen could use.

Item #3: You may wish to divide the students into groups based on the way they answered the questions. The three groups could then debate each of the statements. This is a good time to use effective listening and learn what your students believe to be true. Focus attention on the consequences of drinking — what it does to families, friends, parents and individuals. Use examples from individuals you have known about (no names) and ask the group members to give examples.

Item #4: It is very important for young people to have made their minds up ahead of time about how they are going to respond to the peer pressure to take a drink. Brainstorm different ways to say no to drinking alcohol.

Item #5: Usually, after reading scriptures related to drinking, your students will want to know if Christ drank wine or why he turned water into wine. Be prepared to give them an answer.

To Close the Session:

Young people today equate having fun with drinking and/or drug abuse. "Partying" has become synonymous with getting drunk or "wasted". You may want to emphasize that playing with alcohol is more dangerous than playing with fire. It ruins lives, destroys families, and causes thousands of deaths on the highways each year. Junior high students are especially vulnerable to the addictive properties of alcohol and drugs. Some experts say it takes an adult six months to become addicted, but it takes a teenager only six days. When a young person is growing, the brain is developing as well. Alcohol will affect brain growth and cause permanent brain damage.

Challenge your students to say "no" to drinking. Help them understand that while the Bible does seem to allow for drinking alcohol in certain situations, scripture clearly states "no" for drinking the way most people drink today. (Proverbs 20:1, 23:19-21)

Outside Activities:

1. Have the students create skits that illustrate ways they can say no to drinking.

2. Rent the film "Kevin's Story" from New Day Films, 22 Riverview Drive, Wayne, New Jersey, 07470, and show it to your youth group. It's the story of a high school boy who fatally injured another student while driving under the influence of alcohol and is a powerful film.

Material World

1 Make a list of things you would like to buy if you had all the money you wanted.

_____

_____

_____

2 Circle the statement or statements below that best describe your present financial situation:

a. My family has too much money.

b. I waste a lot of money.

c. My family doesn't have enough money.

d. I wish my family had more money, even though we don't need anything important.

e. I deserve more allowance than the amount I am getting now.

f. I am jealous of other people my age who have more money than I do.

3 Have you ever . . .?

_____ spent money to impress someone.

_____ put more food on your plate than you could eat.

_____ wished you had something you could not afford.

_____ thrown away something valuable.

4 Do you agree or disagree with the following statements?

	Agree	Disagree		Agree	Disagree
a. Being rich is a blessing from God.	_____	_____	**d.** People should share what they have with others.	_____	_____
b. Getting rich is a good way to enjoy life.	_____	_____	**e.** It is wrong to have more money than you need when other people are starving.	_____	_____
c. People have the right to do anything they want with their money.	_____	_____	**f.** Everything we have belongs to God.	_____	_____

5 Choose one of the following scriptures to rewrite in your own words:

Matthew 6:19-21   **Mark 8:34-36**   **I Samuel 2:7-8**

_____

_____

_____

_____

_____

Date Used: _____

Group: _____

MATERIAL WORLD

Topic: Materialism

Purpose of this Session:

This session was designed to help young people understand the material world they live in. The young people of the United States are growing up in a culture of tremendous wealth. Very little time has been spent helping today's youth interpret and understand our materialistic culture.

To Introduce the Topic:

Create a list of all the "things" the students and their families own. Put "Things" or "Stuff" as a heading on newsprint, chalkboard, or overhead projector. You will very likely end up with an extensive list of items. You may wish to illustrate how much we, as American Christians, have.

Another method of introduction is to play a version of "The Price is Right", using pictures of expensive items cut out of magazines for prizes. Or, distribute play money (at random, so some students are "rich" and others are "poor") and have an auction using pictures of the desirable items.

The Discussion:

Item #1: Make a master list of all the things your students wanted to buy. You may wish to have them circle the things on the list they think they "need", as differentiated from the things they "want". This concept is difficult for many young people to grasp and should be discussed.

Item #2: Most of your students will probably declare their parents are keeping them in poverty. Allow them to share their feelings about their personal monetary situation.

Item #3: This item helps young people see they do have a lot in the way of "things". Get them to focus on their feelings. How does it feel to have so much? How does it feel to be envious, jealous, greedy? How do they think children in other cultures, who are not as fortunate, might feel?

Item #4: Ask the students to "vote" on each of the statements, according to the way they answered their TalkSheet. If everyone agrees on a particular statement, proceed to the next. If there is a variety of opinions of a certain one, ask them to defend their points of view. You might wish to have them "take a stand" for their positions. Display the words "Strongly Agree" and "Strongly Disagree" on opposite sides of the room, with "Agree" and "Disagree" somewhere in the middle. The students can then move to stand near the designation of their vote and argue for their reasons.

Item #5: Ask for volunteers to read their versions of the scriptures. Choose one and expound on it in greater depth.

To Close the Session:

Help your group realize money does not buy happiness. If they believe it does, they will always be disappointed in life and feel trapped. The Bible is not neutral on the subject of money. It teaches the worship of money is idolatry. "You cannot serve God and mammon (money/things)." A popular bumper sticker reads, "When you die, whoever has the most stuff wins." Nothing could be further from the truth. Money only buys "things". Happiness and eternal life are not for sale.

Challenge the students as followers of Jesus Christ to change one thing about their lifestyle that would make them a little *less* materialistic. You may wish to brainstorm several ideas to achieve this before you offer the challenge so they have some concrete choices to make.

Outside Activities:

1. A Christian service project that focuses attention on helping the poor would be very appropriate.

2. Ask several group members to create a collage or bulletin board illustrating the materialistic culture of their age group. Then talk about what the collage or bulletin board communicates to others.

TALKING WITH GOD

1 **Complete the following sentence:** If I could pray for only three things, they would be . . .

a. _____

b. _____

c. _____

2 **Is God listening?** Check which statement you believe to be true about your prayers:

a. _____ God hears my prayers and answers them.

b. _____ God hears my prayers, but doesn't always answer them.

c. _____ God doesn't hear my prayers.

3 **Prayer and You.** After each of the following statements, check either "Always", "Sometimes", or "Never".

	ALWAYS	SOMETIMES	NEVER
a. I pray before every meal.	☐	☐	☐
b. I pray while I am at school.	☐	☐	☐
c. I pray for others as well as myself.	☐	☐	☐
d. I praise and thank God in my prayers.	☐	☐	☐
e. I am embarrassed to pray in public.			

4 Eric prayed for a new bicycle for his birthday. He really needed a better-looking bike. He knew God would see that he got the bike. But his birthday came and went, and he didn't get the new bike. Now Eric isn't so sure that prayer makes any difference.

Why do you think Eric didn't get a new bike? _____

_____

How should he feel? _____

_____

What should he do? _____

_____

5 Draw a connecting line between the scripture verse and the appropriate statement.

1. I John 5:14-15	**a. God's peace**
2. I Timothy 2:1-4	**b. Christ's prayer life**
3. Luke 5:16	**c. Pray for others**
4. Philippians 4:6-7	**d. Lord's Prayer**
5. Matthew 6:9-13	**e. God hears our prayers**

TALKING WITH GOD

Topic: Prayer

Purpose of this Session:

Young people often think they don't need to pray or don't feel like praying, even if they think they do need to. But talking and listening to God are important if a Christian is ever going to know God. This TalkSheet offers your group the opportunity to take a closer look at the importance of prayer.

To Introduce the Topic:

Many young people are intimidated and self-conscious about praying in front of others. They also feel guilty when talking about prayer since they do so little of it. In order to overcome these feelings initially, have the group write a personal letter to Jesus. The letter could begin with a greeting. Then they could thank Christ for something He has done in their lives. They could share a happy experience with Him or ask for His opinion on an important issue or decision with which they are struggling. They should be reminded to include any special requests. After the letters have been written, ask for voluteers to read their letters. Then tell them the letters are like prayers.

The Discussion:

Item #1: Make a master list of the things the students chose. Ask why those were their choices. You may want to separate the realistic and necessary requests from those that are not.

Item #2: Ask the students to give examples or reasons for choosing the statements they did. Be prepared to talk about how God answers prayers. Some will have trouble believing God hears their prayers and answers them. A helpful concept is to explain God may answer with a "Yes", a "No", or a "Wait". (This can be discussed even more with Item #4.)

Item #3: Talk about these statements in a general sense. Decide if a junior high student should pray before every meal, pray at school, pray in public, etc. Help them understand they can pray silently when they are walking, or without closing their eyes or bowing their heads or using formal language, etc.

Item #4: This "Tension Getter" gives the group a chance to talk about prayer in a true-to-life situation. Allow the students time to debate their opinions on why Eric didn't get his bike and what he should do. Ask them if they have ever been in a similar situation.

Item #5: Ask for volunteers to share which statements they matched with which verses, then ask them to summarize what they learned about prayer from the scriptures. Ask them to select one Bible verse they would like to discuss further.

To Close the Sesssion:

Encourage your students to begin developing good prayer habits. Remind them it is difficult to have a relationship with God without talking to Him, just as it would be difficult to maintain a friendship without communicating.

Help them understand prayer is not "magic" in the way that muttering magic words and having a genie pop out of a lamp is "magic". Instead, it is a conversation with our loving Father. He wants us to talk with Him, using our own language and sharing deeply with Him.

Instead of challenging the students to do something unrealistic, such as praying for an hour each day, encourage them to begin with two minutes of prayer a day. If they are already praying two, have them strive for four. Challenge them with manageable goals.

A good idea would be to close with "conversational prayer", or sentence prayers, with different volunteers taking turns leading.

Outside Activities:

1. Have your group compile a prayer request list and use it to pray every day for the week.

2. Appoint several students to study the prayer life of Jesus and discuss what they learned the following week.

3. Tape a large sheet of newsprint to the wall in the meeting room. Ask the students to write short messages to Jesus on the paper. Provide marking pens accessible to the "prayer sheet".

WHAT CHANNEL?

1 List five television shows below, from your most favorite to your least favorite:

a. _____

b. _____

c. _____

d. _____

e. _____

2 Answer the following question: If you could spend a day with any television star you chose, who would it be?

_____

3 **I watch:**

    a. far too much television.   **c.** hardly any television.

    b. the right amount of television.   **d.** no television.

If a friend calls while I am watching a good show, I would:

    a. return his or her call after the program.

    b. talk with my friend while continuing to watch the program.

    c. turn the television off and talk to my friend.

    d. (fill in the blank) _____

If your family television set goes on the blink, you would:

    a. talk your parents into buying another set as soon as possible.

    b. find other things to do to occupy my time.

    c. go to a friend's house to watch television.

    d. go crazy!

4 **T.V. and Me:** Check either "That's Me" or "That's Not Me" for each statement below:

	THAT'S ME	THAT'S NOT ME		THAT'S ME	THAT'S NOT ME
a. I watch over 20 hours of television a week.	☐	☐	**d.** I am influenced by what I see on television.	☐	☐
b. I watch TV even though I should be doing something else, like homework.	☐	☐	**e.** I like to watch shows that have a lot of violence and action.	☐	☐
c. I watch shows I know are not good for me.	☐	☐	**f.** I watch rock video shows.	☐	☐
			g. I turn on the TV set as soon as I walk into the house.	☐	☐

5 Decide which of the following scriptures apply to TV viewing and which do not.

    Joshua 14:1-2   **1 Corinthians 10:31**

    Colossians 3:1-2   **Acts 10:4**

Date Used: _____

Group: _____

WHAT CHANNEL?

Topic: Television

Purpose of this Session:

Television. Young people watch a lot of it every day, but rarely do we talk about it at church, except to condemn it. There is a great need for leaders in the church to help young people critically evaluate the programs they watch and make discerning choices. It is unrealistic to expect them to stop watching TV altogether, but it is realistic to believe we can teach them good viewing skills. The purpose of this session is to talk about TV and teach them how to evaluate what they watch.

To Introduce the Topic:

On a large piece of newsprint, or the chalkboard, or an overhead projector, draw a blank television schedule for the week, writing in only the days, certain channels and certain evening times, such as Channel 4, Monday, 7:00 p.m., Channel 10, Tuesday, 8:00 p.m. Then ask the students to guess what shows air at those specific times. You will be surprised how accurate they will be. Have the correct answers available in order to check their responses. Ask the students to rank the shows as good, bad, or questionable. This activity is a great way to begin a discussion on television.

The Discussion:

Item #1: Ask the students to share their answers and to talk about their favorite shows. Ask them to describe why they are their favorites and why they chose one over another.

Item #2: Again, encourage them to share their answers and to talk about their favorite television personalities and why they would want to spend a day with that person. You may learn a lot about your students by listening to them.

Item #3: Use this item to talk about the television-watching habits your students are forming. Many of their evenings revolve around the television screen even when nothing redeeming is playing.

Item #4: This activity provides your students with the opportunity to evaluate their viewing habits. Challenge them to evaluate their own personal habits. Talk about the statements in general terms. Be aware of what the average young person is doing versus what should be done.

Item #5: Ask the students to share the verses that apply to TV and ask how they apply. Let them choose a passage to study, as a group.

To Close the Session:

Help the students understand television watching is not a necessity of life. It is not like eating or sleeping. It is merely entertainment. They do not need to watch television in order to survive — a concept many do not realize.

Point out what they see on fictional television is not real. Everything fictional on television is unreality. Real life is not like a television soap opera or a fictional dramatization. That is exactly the reason television is successful. It offers an escape for those who cannot cope with reality and deals only with the imaginary. Again, many young people do not realize most of what they watch is fantasy, utilizing special effects.

Challenge them to reduce the number of hours they watch television each week. Brainstorm alternative activities as substitutes. Encourage them to set intelligent guidelines for their own television viewing and to evaluate what they do watch in light of their Christian values. Help them realize the values presented on most television programs are more than likely going to be worldly values, not values of the kingdom of God.

Outside Actvities:

Have the group members keep a diary of their weekly viewing habits then bring it in for a discussion. Ask them to discuss the shows they watched and the amount of time they spend sitting in front of the television screen.

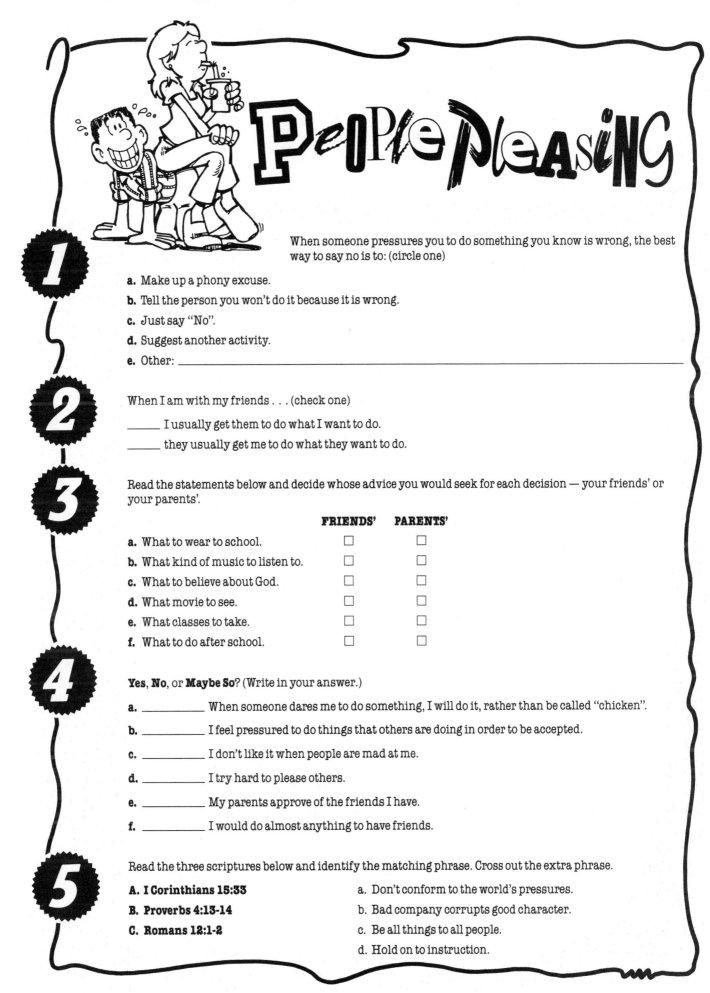

PEOPLE PLEASING

1 When someone pressures you to do something you know is wrong, the best way to say no is to: (circle one)

a. Make up a phony excuse.

b. Tell the person you won't do it because it is wrong.

c. Just say "No".

d. Suggest another activity.

e. Other: _____

2 When I am with my friends . . . (check one)

_____ I usually get them to do what I want to do.

_____ they usually get me to do what they want to do.

3 Read the statements below and decide whose advice you would seek for each decision — your friends' or your parents'.

	FRIENDS'	PARENTS'
a. What to wear to school.	☐	☐
b. What kind of music to listen to.	☐	☐
c. What to believe about God.	☐	☐
d. What movie to see.	☐	☐
e. What classes to take.	☐	☐
f. What to do after school.	☐	☐

4 **Yes**, **No**, or **Maybe So**? (Write in your answer.)

a. _____ When someone dares me to do something, I will do it, rather than be called "chicken".

b. _____ I feel pressured to do things that others are doing in order to be accepted.

c. _____ I don't like it when people are mad at me.

d. _____ I try hard to please others.

e. _____ My parents approve of the friends I have.

f. _____ I would do almost anything to have friends.

5 Read the three scriptures below and identify the matching phrase. Cross out the extra phrase.

A. I Corinthians 15:33

B. Proverbs 4:13-14

C. Romans 12:1-2

a. Don't conform to the world's pressures.

b. Bad company corrupts good character.

c. Be all things to all people.

d. Hold on to instruction.

PEOPLE PLEASING

Topic: Peer Pressure

Purpose of this Session:

The pressure on young people to conform to their peers is steadily increasing. They are experimenting with adult-like behavior at younger and younger ages. Young people spend less and less time interacting with responsible adults. They attend classes with large groups of their peers, work at jobs employing people their age, and go home to empty houses and talk on the phone to their friends. This TalkSheet gives you the opportunity to interact with your youth group on a relevant and significant topic — peer pressure.

To Introduce the Topic:

Announce you are going to conduct a "taste test", like those they have seen on television. Have them taste two different brands of punch, from unmarked pitchers, to determine which is best, Brand A or Brand B.

Ahead of time, tell several of the more "influential" students to choose Brand A and then to try and persuade the others their choice is the best. Chances are many will yield to this "peer pressure" and will also choose Brand A, *even though both brands are exactly the same.*

If the others are not swayed by the pressure, congratulate them for having resisted. Perhaps they will have some insights to share with the rest of the group.

The Discussion:

Item #1: Ask for sharing of specific responses. Suggest a few specific situations, such as "Your friends want to go watch an adult movie on someone's VCR" or "Your friends want you to try smoking marijuana, just to see what it's like." Brainstorm other alternatives to resist peer pressure.

Item #3: Junior high students are in the process of moving away from parental influence and toward peer influence. This does not mean parents are not important to them, but their peers have become a powerful influence as well. This activity allows you to discuss the pressure they face to conform to the wishes of one or the other. Do not ask them to share individually, but discuss each statement in terms of the average teenager. You might wish to ask, "Who won on these items? Your parents or your friends?" (Out of the six items, find out if more were checked "Parents'" or "Friends'".)

Item #4: Again, these statements should be discussed in a general way to avoid embarrassing individuals. Each one deals with a specific aspect of peer pressure. Phrase your questions so they are giving opinions rather than revealing themselves: "What are some things you could do, if your friends called you 'chicken'?" Ask them to think through the consequences of giving in to peer pressure. "And then what?" is a good question for them to ask themselves. Guide them into thinking about the results of their actions.

Item #5: Have the students look up the scriptures and match them to the correct phrases, then discuss each one. In addition, a good one to commit to memory is I Corinthians 15:33.

To Close the Session:

Ask the group to evaluate its responses to the statement in Item #3 and decide how much peer pressure affects them. Explain the difference between being self-controlled (a fruit of the Spirit) and "other-controlled".

Help them realize there is nothing wrong with "doing what your friends do", as long as thos things are not harmful nor displeasing to God. If friends are the source of a negative influence, new friends should be sought.

Encourage your students to listen to their parents' opinions and to consider them, at least, before making a decision. Chances are their parents love them more then their friends do. They should also consult the word of God.

Outside Activities:

Ask the students to interview their parents about peer pressure. They need to ask what kind of peer pressure their parents experienced as young people and what kind they experience as adults.

SO NOBODY'S PERFECT

1 Below, list a few sins common to young people.

a. _____

b. _____

c. _____

d. _____

e. _____

2 What do you think?

	YES, THAT'S ME	NO, THAT'S NOT ME
a. If I sin, God will punish me.	☐	☐
b. When I sin, I feel guilty.	☐	☐
c. I can't stop sinning.	☐	☐
d. I enjoy seeing how much I can get away with.	☐	☐
e. I enjoy doing things I know I shouldn't do.	☐	☐
f. If I knew I could do something wrong without getting caught, I would do it.	☐	☐

3 TRUE or FALSE?

_____ Some sins are worse than others.

_____ Christians do not sin on purpose.

_____ If a sin isn't harmful to anyone, then it's not really a sin.

_____ If you sin accidentally, then it's not really a sin.

_____ If you ask God to forgive your sins, then it's okay to sin again.

4 Read Isaiah 44:6-7 and write its message in your own words.

_____

_____

_____

_____

_____

_____

_____

_____

_____

SO, NOBODY'S PERFECT

Topic: Sin

Purpose of this Session:

Sin is a significant part of the human experience but is not often discussed as such. This TalkSheet is designed to foster an open discussion about sin and what Christian young people can do about it.

To Introduce the Session:

Ask your group to draw what they think "Sin" might look like. Give each a piece of paper and a pencil. When they have completed their drawings, ask several to show theirs to the group.

Pass out newspapers or magazines to the students and ask them how many examples of sin they can find in three minutes. Ask them to share their findings.

The Discussion:

Item #1: Make a master list of all the sins written down. Ask which ones they think are the worst and why they think these sins are so common. Then try to reach a consensus definition of what sin really is — perhaps "a rebellion against God and His divine law."

Item #2: Discuss these statements in a general way rather than a personal one. Do not require the students to reveal their individual answers. Ask questions in this format: "Do you believe God punishes people for sinning, and if so, how?" and "Do you believe it is possible to stop sinning?" Concentrate on why we humans push ourselves to the edge; why we seem to enjoy toying with sin rather than resisting it.

Item #3: As you have the students reveal their answers to these questions, ask them to think of Biblical support for their opinions. It may take a while for them to find suitable scriptures but it will be worth the effort. Spend some extra time on the last statement. Many junior high students lack a good understanding of "repentance" — being truly sorry for their sin and being willing to change.

Item #4: Use this scripture to focus on God's grace and forgiveness. You may also wish to discuss I John 1:9. Have the group members share their paraphrases.

To Close the Session:

Emphasize the fact that sin is a normal part of the human condition. Everyone sins and falls short of the glory of God (I John 1:9). But sin doesn't keep us away from God. We can always get a fresh start when we seek His forgiveness. The saying "Today is the first day of the rest of your life" is especially true for the Christian young person. God allows us to "start over" whenever we ask Him to forgive our sins.

Ask the students to write down one or two sins they worry over or feel guilty about. Tell them what they write will be seen only by themselves and God. They should be specific about the sins and should write "Forgive Me" across the sins. They do not need to sign the papers. Have them fold the papers and turn them in to their group leader, who does not look at their contents. Burn the papers in a Wok or metal trash can, with a fire extinguisher nearby, just in case. If you choose not to burn them, ripping them into tiny pieces works just as well. Either method demonstrates what Christ does with our sins — forgives and forgets. Tell the students they have asked for and received forgiveness from Christ. Now they need to forgive themselves.

Outside Activities:

Ask the students to search scriptures for examples of God's grace and forgiveness, then to share these stories with the group.

We Are The World

1 Make a list of everything in your bedroom.

_____ _____

_____ _____

_____ _____

_____ _____

_____ _____   _____ _____

_____ _____   _____ _____

_____ _____   _____ _____

_____ _____   _____ _____

2 Complete the following sentence:

When I see someone who is really poor . . .

_____ I feel pity for them.   _____ I get angry.   _____ I feel guilty.

_____ I look the other way.   _____ I feel frustrated.   _____ I do whatever I can to help them.

_____ I try to give them something.   _____ I don't care.   _____ Other: _____

3 If you had to be one of the following, which would it be?

_____ Homeless   _____ Hungry and unable to obtain food

_____ Physically handicapped   _____ Old and living in a rest home

_____ Mentally retarded   _____ Sick and unable to afford medical care

4 What do you think?

	THAT'S RIGHT	NO WAY
a. One person cannot make a difference in the world.	☐	☐
b. It is God's will for some people to be poor.	☐	☐
c. Christians should be concentrating on solving the problems of the world.	☐	☐
d. The care of the underprivileged in this country is the responsibility of the government.	☐	☐
e. If someone is poor, it's their own fault.	☐	☐
f. If I could help someone who is poor, sick, or hungry, I would.	☐	☐

5 Choose one of the following scriptures to rewrite in your own words:

Proverbs 14:31   **Proverbs 21:13**   **Isaiah 3:13-15**

_____

_____

_____

_____

WE ARE THE WORLD

Topic: Christian social action

Purpose of this Session:

The present generation of young people has been overwhelmed by the problems of the world and yet, no fuse has been lit underneath them to fire them into action. Junior high students are very idealistic by nature and will respond positively when challenged to "do something important with their lives". Use this TalkSheet to discuss how Christians can make a difference in the world by helping others who are less fortunate.

To Introduce the Session:

Distribute newpapers and newsmagazines (such as TIME and NEWSWEEK) and ask the students to find as many stories as possible about needy people and world problems. Allow five minutes for the search. You can divide them into teams and let them compete to see which team can find the most. Have them share the stories.

Another introduction would be to take a field trip into an area peopled by those who are less fortunate. When you return, the experience should be discussed and the TalkSheet implemented.

The Discussion:

Item #1: Most of your students could fill an entire page with their answers. They can be shown through this activity they have a great deal more than the rest of the world, even though they may not think so. Most young people outside of the United States have little in comparison.

Item #2: Ask for volunteers to share how they completed this sentence. Ask them how they think Christ would have responded to someone who is very poor.

Item #3: Ask the students to reveal their choices. This item forces an empathetic response. Let them talk about their choices as if they were really in that condition. How does it feel? What choices do they have? What will they do? Who will they turn to for help?

Item #4: Ask for opinions on each of these statements, one at a time. These statements deal with how things can and should be changed. Remember, the young people of today need to know they can make a difference, in spite of the overwhelming nature of the world's problems. Spend extra time on the last statement. Ask them for ideas to help someone less fortunate than they.

Item #5: Have several volunteers share their versions of the scriptures. Ask them to state one thing they learned from the passages.

To Close the Session:

Focus on the fact that God wants to use each person in the room to make a difference in the world. You might want to remind them of the "Feeding of the Five Thousand" story in the Bible. Jesus was able to use one boy's small sack lunch and feed a multitude with it. In the same way, God can take whatever we have to offer him and bless it. Even though it doesn't look like anything, "little is much".

Outside Activities:

Planning a mission or service project is an obvious response to this session. An excellent resource for ideas on planning and projects is the book entitled *Ideas for Social* Action by Anthony Campolo (Youth Specialties/Zondervan, 1984). Involve the students in the planning stage so they have some ownership of the project.

CHRIS-TI-AN-I-TY

1

Jennifier goes to church almost every Sunday with her parents. She doesn't always understand the sermons, but she likes the singing. She doesn't attend the youth group meetings. At school, she is a good student and never gives anyone any trouble. She has lots of friends.

Do you think Jennifer is a Christian?

_____ **Yes**　　_____ **No**　　_____ **I don't know**

2

In order to be a Christian, you must . . .(Check those you believe necessary to be considered a Christian.)

_____ be baptized.
_____ be confirmed.
_____ ask Jesus into your heart.
_____ believe the Bible is true.
_____ be a church member.
_____ stop committing sins.
_____ be born again.

_____ belong to the right kind of church.
_____ repent.
_____ love God and love your neighbor.
_____ act like a Christian.
_____ give money to the church.
_____ read the Bible and pray every day.

3

People should become Christians because . . . (choose the best reason from the list below.)

_____ they will go to heaven.
_____ they will have a better life on earth.
_____ they will experience the love of God in their lives.

4

Complete this sentence: "One thing I don't understand about the Christian faith is . . ."

_____
_____
_____
_____
_____
_____

5

Match the following scripture verses with the statements in the right-hand column.

1. Matthew 22:39   a. Love others

2. Romans 12:1-2   b. Follow Christ

3. Matthew 22:37   c. Glorify God

4. Matthew 6:33   d. Love God

5. I Corinthians 10:31 e. God's kingdom

6. Matthew 16:24   f. God's will

Date Used: _____

Group: _____

CHRIS·TI·AN·I·TY

Topic: Basic Christianity

Purpose of this Session:

This TalkSheet was designed to help explore some of the basic ideas about Christianity. Feel free to emphasize specific beliefs or doctrines within the context of this worksheet.

There is a diversity of viewpoints among Christians concerning some of the issues raised on this TalkSheet, so before using it, some homework on your part is highly recommended. Do the activities on the TalkSheet yourself first and look up all the questions you might feel indefinite about in the Bible.

To Introduce the Session:

Ask one of the respected adult members of the church or a youth sponsor to prepare a five-minute sermon. It should contain several half-truths that are not Biblically correct. They should be somewhat subtle so as not to appear obvious. See how long it takes your students to disagree with the sermon, if they do at all. Another method of introduction is to make up a short quiz on Christianity and find out how informed your students are.

The Discussion:

Item #1: This "Tension Getter" was designed to help your students explore what it really means to be a Christian. If most of them choose "I don't know", you might add more information about Jennifer, a little at a time. Mention she was baptized as an infant; she doubts the Bible is really the word of God; she went forward to receive Christ at a Billy Graham crusade; she sometimes swears and has started smoking cigarettes, etc. The main point to emphasize is that it is very difficult to judge others and to know whether or not they are "real" Christians or not. That is God's prerogative, not ours.

Item #2: Ask which statements on this list are *necessary* in order to be a Christian, talking about each in turn. As you discuss these, it would be wise to have verifying scripture handy to arrive at a consensus with the group. Be careful not to end up with a long list of "necessary things" that portrays Christianity as a legalistic religion, which it is not. Try to distill the consensus into the essentials and help them understand why some of the other things are also important.

Item #3: Ask the students to reveal their answers. Help them see that the Christian faith, while it does promise eternal life and a better quality of life here on earth, is primarily concerned with our fellowship with God, our loving heavenly Father.

Item #4: Use this opportunity to clear up misunderstandings your students might have regarding the Christian life. Before you answer questions, ask them to share their views and understandings with each other. Don't be too quick to give answers when you might be better off saying "I don't know" or "I don't understand, either". Perhaps during the week, you or the students can do some more research to find the answers.

Item #5: After the students have completed matching up the verses with the statements, choose one or two to study more closely.

To Close the Session:

Invite those students who are not Christians or who are not sure of their faith to talk with you further about the Christian experience. Assure them it is not necessary to understand everything there is to know about the Christian faith in order to live a successful Christian life. Even the great theologians struggle with doctrinal issues. Karl Barth summed up the Christian faith in this manner: "Jesus loves me, this I know, for the Bible tells me so." It really boils down to that.

Encourage your students to grow in the Christian faith, to study the scriptures and to pray, in order to have a better understanding of what it means for them. They should know enough about basic Christianity to be able to share their faith with others.

Outside Activities:

1. Assign small groups to research specific Christian doctrine and report back to the youth group with a presentation of what was learned. Possible topics could be sanctification, conversion, revelation, creation, etc.

2. Assign several students book reports on books about Christian life, and have them read the reports to the youth group.

3. Have the students write a letter outlining their plan to grow as Christians. Give them envelopes, which they will address to themselves and seal. Mail the letters to them in six months.

WISE UP

1 If you had an important decision to make, to whom would you go for advice? (Circle the best three choices.)

Mother **Best Friend** **Pastor** **Grandparent** **Father**

Youth Pastor **Teacher** **School Counselor** **Boyfriend**

Girlfriend **Coach** **My Dog** **Fortune Teller** **Nobody**

2 I need to show more wisdom in . . . (check all that apply):

____ doing my school work   ____ handling my feelings
____ choosing my friends   ____ listening to advice
____ my family life   ____ planning my time
____ my use of money   ____ other: _____

3 Which of the things listed below would help you become a wiser person? (Choose three)

____ **a.** Reading more books   ____ **d.** Watching more television   ____ **g.** Thinking before I act
____ **b.** Taking more risks   ____ **e.** Choosing wiser friends   ____ **h.** Going with my feelings
____ **c.** Praying more often   ____ **f.** Asking more questions   ____ **i.** Studying the Bible more often.

4 Dear Junior High student:

I am a mother of three kids — two teenaged daughters and one teenaged son. My problem is that none of them will listen to my advice. They think they know it all and I know nothing, especially the oldest, my son. I love them and am concerned for their future and want to give them some of my wisdom. I don't want them to make the same mistakes I made or those I've seen others make. What can I do?

At The End of My Rope

What advice would you give this mother?

_____

_____

_____

5 Match the scripture verses on the left with the statements on the right.

1. **Proverbs 10:19**   a. **Talking too much**
2. **Proverbs 12:22**   b. **Trusting in God**
3. **Proverbs 13:20**   c. **Listening to parents**
4. **Proverbs 3:5-6**   d. **Answering gently**
5. **Proverbs 22:24-25**   e. **Having wise friends**
6. **Proverbs 15:1**   f. **Being angry**
7. **Proverbs 1:8**   g. **Lying**

Date Used: _____

Group: _____

WISE UP

Topic: Wisdom

Purpose of this Session:

The young people of today get advice from friends, teachers, parents, and the media, just to name a few sources. To whom will they listen? This session was created to discuss the need for guidance in one's life. This TalkSheet was designed to end with a discussion on God's word as the ultimate source of wisdom.

To Introduce this Session:

Before the session begins, ask several of your students to write out some of the dumbest things they've ever done, keeping their statements as brief as possible and unsigned. Inform them the situations will be read aloud. Before distributing the TalkSheets, read the experiences to the group and see if they can guess who wrote each one. Then disclose the author and applaud him or her. Don't let the group ridicule anyone. This can be a fun way to introduce a discussion on wisdom — focusing on the stupid things we sometimes do.

The Discussion:

Item #1: Ask the students to share their choices of sources for advice. Make a master list and find out who your group considers the best "advice giver".

Item #2: Let the students share with each other the different areas where they need to show more wisdom. Share some of your own high school experiences when you should have made a wiser choice and discuss how that experience affects you today.

Item #3: Find out how this question was answered, then discuss each item, one at a time. Encourage those that are positive "wisdom-builders" (a,c,e,f,g,i) and discuss why the others are not so advisable.

Item #4: This letter from a mother deals with a common problem of parents of teenagers — the know-it-all son or daughter. As the students share their advice to this mother, help them see the parents' point of view rather than just their own. Parents need support from youth leaders as they attempt to guide their children.

Item #5: The focus here is using the Bible as a source of wisdom for guiding our daily lives. Young people need to be encouraged to look at God's word to help them in practical ways.

To Close the Session:

Talk about the importance of seeking God's wisdom through prayer, Bible study, and the counsel of other Christians. Challenge your students to be intelligently appraising of the advice they get from their friends, the media, etc. They should rely on their own judgment to evaluate all of it. Remind them the wisest proverb of all is "The fear of God is the beginning of wisdom." (Prov. 1:7) This means true wisdom comes from God and the more we love God and keep his commandments, the more wisdom we receive.

Outside Activities:

1. Brainstorm five topics young people want to get advice about — choosing friends, dealing with anger, drugs, etc. Then assign scriptures for them to research illustrating how the Bible treats each one. (Use a Topical Bible or some other reference book to select scriptures.) Have the students report their findings.

2. Place a large piece of newsprint on the wall in the meeting room upon which the students can write different words of advice they have heard or read. After several weeks, discuss some of the advice in light of God's word.

ONE IS A LONELY NUMBER

1 Circle any of the following words that best describe LONELINESS to you.

depression	rejection	hurt	boredom	time with God
happy	peaceful	sadness	quiet	frightened	fun

2 **TRUE or FALSE?**

_____ **a.** Being alone is the same as being lonely.

_____ **b.** Being bored is the same as being lonely.

3 Do you **AGREE** or **DISAGREE** with the statements below?

	AGREE	DISAGREE
a. Everyone is lonely at times.	_____	_____
b. If you are with other people, you won't be lonely.	_____	_____
c. If you feel lonely, it's your own fault.	_____	_____
d. Jesus felt lonely.	_____	_____

4 Who are the loneliest people in the world? (Rank the following from "1" — loneliest — to "6" — least lonely.)

_____ widows and widowers   _____ young people

_____ famous people   _____ old people

_____ divorced people   _____ Christians

5 Read I Kings 19:9-18, then see if you can write a comforting postcard to Elijah.

Dear Elijah,

BEERSHEBA 8050 7D
PM
28 SOL
988

JUDA
22

Date Used: _____

Group: _____

ONE'S A LONELY NUMBER

Topic: Loneliness

Purpose of this Session:

Adults tell young people the teen years are the best years of their lives. Adults forget these years can be very lonely in the midst of the carefree fun. This TalkSheet offers your group the chance to talk about their lonely feelings, the causes and cures of loneliness and how God can help.

To Introduce the Session:

Tell the students they are going to make up a progressive story about loneliness. Begin the story by saying, "Skip was getting ready to go to school, when. . ." then let a student proceed with the plot, continuing around the group. The only rules are the story should be kept clean and be about loneliness. You will end up with a lonely story and a good lead-in to the discussion.

The Discussion:

Item #1: Ask the students to share and explain their choices. Ask if any other words came to mind and make a master list of all the words thought of.

Item #2: Young people often assume if they are bored or alone, then they are lonely. They need to understand they don't always have to be entertained or be with a crowd. In fact, they can be entertained or with their friends and still feel lonely.

Item #3: Focus on "b" and talk about being alone and being lonely. A person can be alone and not be lonely. Also focus on the fact that Christ felt lonely. 'See Matthew 13:53-57, Luke 4:24-30, Mark 14:22, 27, 31, 50, Mark 15:1-34.) In today's world, young people believe they must be entertained constantly. They suffer from stimulus overload and don't know how to deal with periods of being quiet or being alone. Help them understand they need times of "alone-ness" and that these "lonely" times are not bad. They can be very healthy. Learning to be content when alone is one of the first signs of real maturity.

Item #4: Have the students share their choices and explain why they ranked them in the order they chose. Ask how loneliness could be remedied for each type of person.

Item #5: Help the students understand Elijah's situation. After they have had some time to write their postcards, have them read them aloud. Ask if they have ever felt like Elijah. Brainstorm practical and concrete solutions to loneliness. Some possible solutions are prayer, not comparing oneself to others, enjoying solitude, reading a psalm, talking with parents, and reaching out to help others.

To Close the Session:

Help the students understand when they are lonely, Christ is with them. They may feel lonely, but they are never alone. Encourage them to remember to take advantage of their lonely times by taking time for prayer.

Emphasize that the main reason we experience a feeling such as loneliness is our gregariousness. God created us to have good and close relationships with other people. We were created to live in families and in community with others. That's why it's important to protect our relationships and to do whatever we can to improve them. Close by using a community-building activity. Hundreds of them can be found in the *IDEAS* series published by Youth Specialties.

Outside Activities:

Have the students schedule an hour of their time in a "lonely place", away from everyone, without radio, television or any other distraction. Have them concentrate on being alone with themselves, just sitting and thinking or praying. Have them share their thoughts about the experience afterward.

LOOKING FOR LOVE

1 Love is _____. (Choose the word you
think best from those listed below.)

patient　　**courteous**　　**caring**　　**trusting**　　**helpful**　　**jealous**　　**romantic**

forever　　**honest**　　**accepting**　　**exciting**　　**obedient**　　**giving**　　**kind**

2 It is impossible to love certain people.
_____ **True**　　　　_____ **False**

3 Rank the following from the **easiest** to love (1) to the **most difficult** to love (5).

_____ mother

_____ sister/brother

_____ father

_____ God

_____ best friend

4 Check any of the following you consider examples of Christian love.

_____ Making a joke out of a mistake someone makes.

_____ Giving money to the church.

_____ Trying to help someone who is in trouble.

_____ Being nice to people who are nice to you.

_____ Eating lunch with someone who is a "loner".

_____ Doing your chores at home.

_____ Getting even with someone who has hurt you.

_____ Not squealing on someone who has done something wrong.

_____ Sharing your faith with your friends.

_____ Talking about someone behind their back.

_____ Letting someone copy your homework.

5 Read I John 4:7-12 and write a one-sentence summary of it below:

_____

_____

_____

_____

LOOKING FOR LOVE

Topic: Christian love

Purpose of this Session:

Love is something we talk about often but the subject still confuses many young people. They often think it is some kind of gushy, sentimental emotion you have toward someone else rather than an act of obedience to God. This TalkSheet will help you find out what your students think about love. It will also give them a chance to talk about practical ways they can put love into effect.

To Introduce the Topic:

Most of today's popular music deals with romantic love. Begin this session by listening to a song together or by watching a music video that deals with love.

Another lead-in is to have the students make an "I Love. . ." bumper sticker — with a red heart instead of the word "love" — and complete the sentence any way they wish. Have each person share their "love" with the rest of the group.

The Discussion:

Item #1: Have the students share their choices and explain why they chose them. Save your comments for later.

Item #2: Young people often believe love is finding something about another person that is lovable and only then can they love that person. Christian, or agape , love says we don't look for a lovable quality, but we love in spite of lovable characteristics. Talk about this concept of love with your group.

Item #3: Have the students share their reasons for their answers. Make this a fun activity.

Item #4: Go through this list and see how many selected each one as an example of Christian love. Discuss those in which there is not complete agreement. Brainstorm additional examples of love and talk about them in terms of practical ways to demonstrate Christian love.

Item #5: Have the students share what they learned from reading this passage. Focus on the idea that we love others because God loves us all.

To Close the Session:

Challenge your students to look at people the way Christ did. Every person is a child of God, created in the image of God, and is someone for whom Christ died. Our culture teaches using people and loving things, but the Christian way is just the opposite.

Help your students see that love is not a feeling or an emotion, but a decision we make. The Bible doesn't ask that we "like" our neighbor, but it does command us to love even those we don't like. That is the mark of the Christian — that we love others as we love ourselves.

Outside Activities:

1. Have each group member choose one person they think is difficult to love. During the week, they can try to express love in some fashion to this person.

2. Have your students visit elderly congregation members to clean their yards and homes as expressions of love.

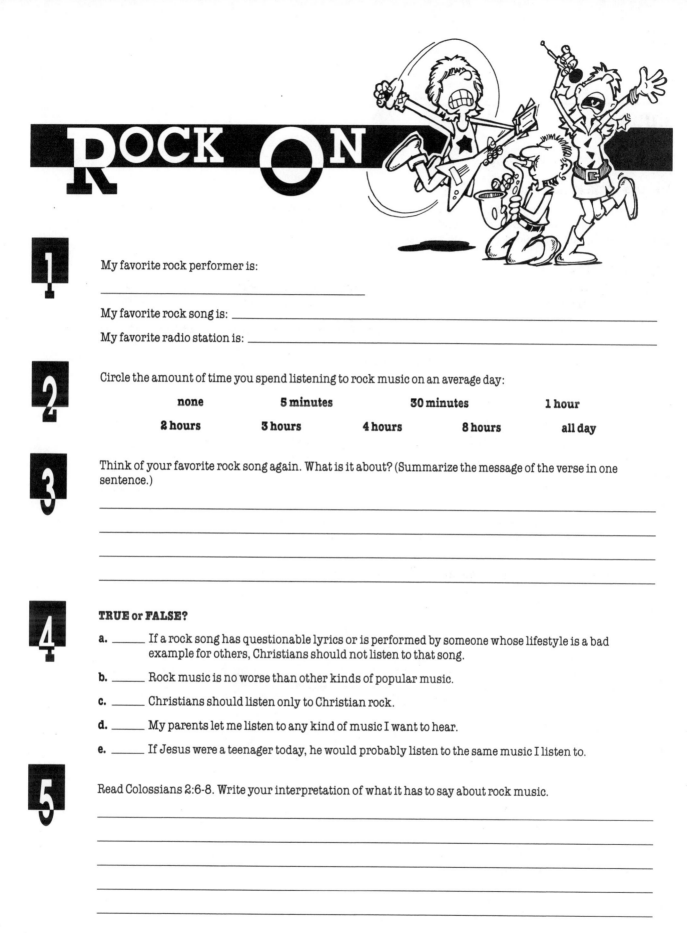

ROCK ON

1 My favorite rock performer is:

_____

My favorite rock song is: _____

My favorite radio station is: _____

2 Circle the amount of time you spend listening to rock music on an average day:

none	5 minutes	30 minutes	1 hour
2 hours	3 hours	4 hours	8 hours	all day

3 Think of your favorite rock song again. What is it about? (Summarize the message of the verse in one sentence.)

_____

_____

_____

_____

4 **TRUE or FALSE?**

a. _____ If a rock song has questionable lyrics or is performed by someone whose lifestyle is a bad example for others, Christians should not listen to that song.

b. _____ Rock music is no worse than other kinds of popular music.

c. _____ Christians should listen only to Christian rock.

d. _____ My parents let me listen to any kind of music I want to hear.

e. _____ If Jesus were a teenager today, he would probably listen to the same music I listen to.

5 Read Colossians 2:6-8. Write your interpretation of what it has to say about rock music.

_____

_____

_____

_____

_____

ROCK ON

Topic: Rock-n-Roll music

Purpose of this Sesssion:

Rock music often polarizes young people and adults in the church. Most young people identify with their peer group by listening to the same music as their friends. Most teens listen to rock, even if they don't like it. This TalkSheet was designed to facilitate a balanced discussion with regard to rock-n-roll music.

To Introduce the Topic:

Begin the evening by listening to a few rock albums. Ask the students to bring their favorite tapes and records. They like the volume turned up loud, so you may decide to humor them for this discussion, to help you — and them — better understand the music that permeates the youth culture.

If available, bring a few records you enjoyed as a teenager. Most young people are familiar with the music of the '50s, '60s and '70s.

It is important to introduce this discussion in a positive way, without the young people feeling their music is being criticized. Try to be objective and listen effectively to the students.

The Discussion:

Item #1: This exercise will be fun. Have the students share their favorites and tell why they chose them. Tally the results on the board and find out which performers, songs, and radio stations get the most votes.

Item #2: Find out what time of day your students listen to rock — before school, during lunch, only on weekends, etc. Do they listen mostly to records? Tapes? The radio? A Walkman? Compare how much time they spend listening to music with how much time they spend doing other things, such as watching TV, working, homework, family activities, Bible study, prayer, etc.

Item #3: This question may reveal many do not even know what the message of a certain song is. On the other hand, it may reveal your students enjoy songs with suggestive or questionable lyrics. Let them decide if they are good or bad songs.

Item #4: Read each statement aloud and find out what your students think about each. Reserve your own comments until the conclusion.

Item #5: Ask a few volunteers to read their applications of this scripture to their music.

To Close the Sesssion:

Rock music, as a style, is no more of an evil in and of itself than bluegrass or classical music. To try and convince young people otherwise is not only wrong but pointless. What is important is to help them use discretion about the kind of music they choose to listen to and for them to resist peer pressure. It isn't wrong to like rock (or jazz or anything else, for that matter), but it is wrong for Christians to spend time and money embracing anything that undermines the values of the kingdom of God.

Good guideline questions for them to ask themselves are: "Does this music draw me closer or farther away from God?" and "Does the song support or oppose Christian values?" The students should decide.

Now is the time for you to state your values and opinions regarding rock. You may wish to play some Christian rock to close the session, especially if your students are not familiar with contemporary Christian rock music. If you are not familiar with it either, visit a Christian book store and ask what is available.

Outside Activities:

1. Have the group study the "Top 40" list of current rock hits and rate each song according to the content of the lyrics, the lifestyles of the artists, the music itself, and any other criteria desired. List them from best to worst, creating your own "Youth Group Top 40" which can be distributed to group members and radio stations in your area.

2. Menconi Ministries (P.O Box 306, Cardiff-by-the-Sea, CA, 92007-0831) provides videos, tapes, and other materials about rock music which can be used for further discussion. Menconi also publishes the "Hot 200", short profiles of current rock stars.

LET'S GET PHYSICAL

1 The most handsome guy in the world is _____

_____

The most beautiful girl in the world is _____

_____

2 Which of the following is most important to you? Rank them from **1** (most important) to **7** (least important).

_____ My looks

_____ My abilities

_____ My personality

_____ My intelligence

_____ My health

_____ My wealth

_____ My relationship with God

3 Complete this sentence:
If I could change one thing about the way I look, it would be . . .

_____

_____

4 YES or NO?

_____ **a.** The last thing I usually do before leaving my home is look in the mirror.

_____ **b.** Good looking people have more friends.

_____ **c.** People judge others by their physical attractiveness.

_____ **d.** I usually feel self-conscious about the way I look.

_____ **e.** I enjoy dressing to attract attention to myself.

_____ **f.** It's okay to wear the latest fashions and fads.

_____ **g.** Sometimes I wish I looked like someone else.

_____ **h.** I don't let a person's appearance affect the way I think of him or her.

5 Read the following verses and summarize each of their messages in five words or less.

Proverbs 31:30 _____

I Samuel 16:7 _____

Date Used: _____

Group: _____

LET'S GET PHYSICAL

Topic: Physical appearance

Purpose of this Session:

One's own physical appearance is very important to self-esteem, especially to the adolescent. This session gives your students the opportunity to appraise physical appearance and how their attitude toward it affects them as Christians.

To Introduce the Topic:

Before this session — for dramatic effect — dress yourself very differently from your usual attire and change your hairstyle. Ask the students what they think of your new look. Your physical appearance makes a statement about the kind of person you are. Ask your group what your new look says about you.

The Discussion:

Item #1: Make this item fun. Have the students elect the best looking people in the world. Discuss why they are so good looking.

Item #2: It is doubtful anyone will put "looks" as their number one choice. Probably "relationship with God" will get the highest rankings, which is predictable. Take this opportunity to point out our actions indicate the opposite most of the time. How much time each day do we spend on our appearances? Probably a lot more than we spend on improving our relationship with God.

Item #3: Everyone dislikes something about their own appearance. You might share something you would like to change about your own physical appearance, then allow volunteers in the group to do the same. Point out everyone, even glamourous movie stars, feel they have defects that need to be corrected. Most of the time, our so-called defects are really assets and don't need to be changed at all.

Item #4: Since personal appearance can be difficult to discuss, talk about these statements in a general way. Don't ask for personal examples; let those be volunteered without being requested. Don't be afraid to deal with the hurt, anger and frustration many of your students feel about their appearances. Stress God's love and acceptance. Understand even the students you consider "good looking" will have hang-ups about their appearance.

Item #5: Have the group summarize these two passages and ask for examples of how the verses could be applied to daily living.

To Close the Session:

Summarize the most important points the students have discovered in the discussion. Some to emphasize are: God cares about our minds and souls more than our looks; it's okay to try to look our best, but we shouldn't become obsessed with our appearance; God wants us to look good both on the inside and the outside. Christians differ from the rest of the world because we accept each other and love each other no matter how we look. Keep your closing remarks upbeat and full of affirmation.

Outside Activities:

1. Have the students cut out examples of physical preoccupation from magazine ads and bring them to the meeting. Then you can lead a discussion about the magazine ads placing more emphasis on physical appearance rather than on the product they are trying to sell.

2. Ask the students to find several rock songs whose lyrics place emphasis on physical attractiveness. Listen to the words and discuss them with the group.

SO WHAT'S THE DIFFERENCE?

1 It is _____ for me to live like a "good Christian".

_____ **easy**   _____ **hard**   _____ **impossible**

2 If you don't act like a Christian, then you are not a Christian.

_____ **TRUE**   _____ **FALSE**

3 Check all of the following statements that describe how you think Christians should live.

_____ Wear clothes that are the latest style.

_____ Copy whatever their friends do.

_____ Stand up and defend their beliefs.

_____ Listen to the advice of their parents.

_____ Go to church.

_____ Witness to others by their actions and their words.

_____ Care only about people who will care about them.

_____ Get good grades.

_____ Watch whatever is popular on television.

_____ Say things they think others want to hear.

_____ Listen to God's word by reading the Bible.

_____ Make fun of the weird kids at school.

4 Eric attends church every Sunday and is a leader in his youth group. All the adults at church are proud of Eric because he is "such a fine Christian young man". When Eric goes to school, however, none of his friends even know he is a Christian because he acts just like everyone else.

What is your opinion of Eric? _____

_____

_____

5 Which of the following verses warn against hypocrisy?

Matthew 6:1   **Matthew 23:1-4**

Matthew 7:15   **Matthew 25:40**

Matthew 11:28

SO, WHAT'S THE DIFFERENCE?

Topic: Hypocrisy

Purpose of this Session:

As children grow into adolescence, they develop the capacity for reflective thinking. One of the many things they begin to scrutinize is how they and others live out their lives. They may express the highest of ideals, yet be unable to carry them out. This session provides you with the opportunity to discuss how your students live out their Christian beliefs.

To Introduce the Session:

The following skit is a fun way to approach this discussion:
Brian: Hi, Tom! How are you doing?
Tom: Not too good, Brian. I've got a six-week's test in math tomorrow and I'm not ready for it.
Brian: Hey, well, like I'm really good in math. I'll help you study anytime you want. Just say the word, and I'll be there, man. What are best friends for, anyway?
Tom: Hey, that's great. I really appreciate that! How about tonight, so I can cram for the test. Say around seven?
Brian: Gee, sorry, pal. Can't make it. I'm busy tonight.
Tom: Oh. Well, uh, how about tomorrow morning, early, before school?
Brian: NO WAY, man! My eyes don't focus until after lunch!
Tom: Oh. Well, thanks anyway, I guess. See you later.
Brian: You bet, man! And, like, good luck on the test, you know?

After the skit, ask the students what they thought of Brian. Ask if they would like to have him as a friend and why or why not. They will probably focus on how Brian said one thing and did another, which is a good lead-in for a discussion on hypocrisy.

The Discussion:

Item #1: Have the students share their completed sentences with each other. Discuss the fact that the Christian life is not easy to live and no one ever promised us it would be. It is very hard and, therefore, not surprising that we blow it a good deal of the time. But that doesn't mean we should stop trying to do it right.

Item #2: This issue could lead to a fairly intense discussion on a major theological issue: salvation by faith versus salvation by good works. Don't let the discussion drift that far. Just make the point that God loves us as we are and not as we should be. No one is able to live a flawless Christian life. Our goal is to live more and more like Christ wants us to, but we don't have to be perfect all the time in order to call ourselves Christians.

Item #3: Discuss each statement and ask why the students checked or did not check each one. Use this item to discuss Christian conduct. Do not focus only on things Christians should not do. Explore the things Christians can and should do because they are Christians.

Item #4: Ask the students to share their opinion of Eric. Ask them why they think Eric lives two different lives and what are some ways he could let his friends at school know he is a Christian. How should Eric's life be different?

Item #5: Ask the students to look up the scriptures and read those that pertain to hypocrisy. Ask them explain their meanings, if they can.

To Close the Session:

Close the discussion with a challenge to your group members to "practice what they preach". Leave room in your challenge for God's forgiveness. None of us exemplify God's ideal in our lives. Also leave room in your closing statements for tolerance — within reason — for other Christians.

Emphasize it may be easy to fake others out and to pretend to be something we are not, but God does not look at the outward appearance. He looks within us and knows how we really are.

Outside Activities:

Ask your youth group to think of one thing they each can do during the next week to put their faith into practice. They can report on the results at the next meeting.

The Devil Made Me Do It

1 Place a check in the appropriate column as to whether or not you are ever TEMPTED to do anything on the list:

YES, A LOT	SOMETIMES	NO, NEVER	
_____	_____	_____	Tell a lie.
_____	_____	_____	Cheat on a test or homework.
_____	_____	_____	Sneak food from the fridge.
_____	_____	_____	Smoke.
_____	_____	_____	Look at porno magazines or videos.
_____	_____	_____	Do what my friends are doing, even if it's wrong.
_____	_____	_____	Pretend to be sick to avoid going to school.
_____	_____	_____	Do drugs.
_____	_____	_____	Shoplift.
_____	_____	_____	Gossip about a friend.
_____	_____	_____	Use foul language.
_____	_____	_____	Drink alcohol.
_____	_____	_____	Go too far with sex.
_____	_____	_____	Steal money from my parents.

2 Complete these sentences:

I am tempted to do bad things . . .
_____ more now than I used to be.
_____ about the same now as I used to be.
_____ less now than I used to be.

When I give in to temptation, I usually feel . . .
_____ ashamed of myself.
_____ proud of myself.
_____ okay about myself.

Most of the time, when I am tempted . . .
_____ I think about it a long time.
_____ I give in right away.
_____ I try to ignore the temptation.
_____ I read my Bible and pray.

3 **TRUE or FALSE?**

_____ **a.** Sometimes God tempts you as a test, to see if you will resist.
_____ **b.** It's a sin to be tempted to do bad things.
_____ **c.** Christians are tempted as often as non-Christians.
_____ **d.** Some temptations are too hard to resist.
_____ **e.** Temptation comes from the devil.
_____ **f.** If you give in to temptation, it's the devil's fault.

4 Complete the paragraph below, using what you learn from reading the following scriptures: I Corinthians 10:13, Luke 22:46, Psalm 119:11, and James 4:7.

"How to Handle Temptation"

One way to resist temptation is to _____.

Another way is to _____. I know

that when I am tempted, God will _____.

If I resist temptation, I know the devil will _____

THE DEVIL MADE ME DO IT

Topic: Temptation

Purpose of this Session:

Pearl S. Buck once wrote, "Youth is the age of temptation". Temptation is a big part of an adolescent's life. As they gain more independence from their parents and approach adulthood, they experience temptations they never had before. In addition, because of their newly-acquired ability to think on an abstract level, they experience turmoil and guilt they never felt as children. Use this TalkSheet to talk about temptation with your group members in a helpful and supportive atmosphere.

To Introduce the Topic:

A fun way to begin is to subject your students to "temptation". Ask for three volunteers and explain the following scenario to them, to be acted out: A man accidentally drops a ten-dollar bill while walking. A junior high student sees the money on the ground, which the man doesn't notice. What should he do?

One of the volunteers pretends to be the "devil" and one the "angel"; they stand on each side of the tempted student. The devil tries to convince him to keep the money ("finders keepers") and the angel insists he return it to its rightful owner. Encourage your "actors" to make convincing arguments. The student must decide what to do.

The Discussion:

Item #1: Rather than being specific, ask how many items were checked in each column. Some students might reveal which items they are never tempted to do, but most will be embarrassed to admit which ones they are often tempted to do.

Item #2: Ask for volunteers to share their answers, without forcing anyone to participate. Make a point of stating they will probably face more temptation now than they did when they were younger. Brainstorm ways to resist temptation when discussing the second sentence. On the last sentence, state guilt and shame are normal, but if we are truly sorry, God will forgive us and take away our guilt.

Item #3: Help the students realize temptation is Satan's way of trying to steal them away from God. Satan cannot *make* us do anything, so we cannot blame Satan when we choose to sin, but Satan will tempt us through our weaknesses. God never tempts us, but Satan does.

Item #4: Ask the students to read their completed sentences based on the scriptures.

To Close the Session:

Emphasize the fact that temptation is a normal part of growing up. The students need to know God has given them free will. The choice is theirs. And the choices they make today will affect them in the future. Encourage them to live the Christian life with the power of the Holy Spirit as much as possible. They can resist temptation much more forcefully if they memorize scripture, pray, and continue to grow in their faith. The only way to resist is to stay close to Christ, the only Man in history who has ever beat the devil on his own turf. Christ can give them the strength to make the right choices.

Outside Activities:

Have the students keep a diary during the week, writing down the times they are tempted and the times they were able to resist. Have them share their diaries at the next meeting.

GOD IN A BOD

1 Circle the words below that you think best describes Jesus. Cross out those that don't fit Jesus at all.

| Meek | Strong | Strange | Sad | Fun | Tough | Cool | Humble |

Mysterious   Boring   Friendly   Happy   Angry   Smart

Honest   Awesome   Wimpy   Loving   God

2 Pretend Jesus Christ is presently living in your town, attending your school and is the same age as you.

Would he be popular or unpopular? _____

Where would He go to church? _____

What kind of music would He listen to? _____

What would He do after school? _____

What TV shows would He watch, if any? _____

If He attended your youth group, would He like it? _____

3 If someone asked you why you believed in Jesus, what would you tell them? _____

_____

_____

_____

_____

_____

_____

_____

_____

_____

4 Christ asked his disciples, "Who do people say that I am?" (Matthew 16:13). Find out what each of the following Bible verses says about Christ, then complete each of the sentences.

John 10:30   Jesus is _____

_____

Colossians 1:13-23   Jesus is _____

_____

John 3:16-17   Jesus is _____

_____

Matthew 16:16   Jesus is _____

_____

GOD IN A BOD

Topic: Jesus Christ

Purpose of this Session:

On of the best studies you can instigate with junior high students is on the life of Christ. As their thinking ability matures, they have a great need to re-discover the Christ they have encountered previously only in Bible stories and in Sunday School lessons. Who is He? This TalkSheet was designed to focus attention on Christ, His attributes, and how the students can learn to know Him personally.

To Introduce the Topic:

Assemble several familiar pictures of Jesus. Some depict Him as "meek and mild", others show Him suffering, and still others show Him laughing. Ask the group to decide which is the most accurate portrayal of their idea of the real Jesus Christ.

Another lead-in is to give the students a list of events during the life of Christ, such as His baptism, the Sermon on the Mount, different miracles, parables, etc. Divide the group into competing teams which will try to arrange the events chronologically. The right answers are available in a Bible dictionary, a parallel version of the New Testament, or some other resource dealing with the life of Christ.

The Discussion:

Item #1: Ask the students to reveal the words they circled and the words they crossed out. Ask them to give reasons for their answers. Have them think of other words to describe Jesus.

Item #2: This can be fun and can help the students think of Christ as more than just an historical figure. Ask what kind of person they think Jesus would be if He were living today, in their town. Try to get away from the "Jesus in the carpenter shop" mind-set and think of Him as a modern-day teenager. This may be difficult for them to do, but reassure them there is no right or wrong answer. Simply try to picture Jesus in today's world and have them give reasons for their descriptions. If possible, ask them to recall scripture to substantiate their ideas.

Item #3: Ask for several different responses. It would be wise for you to prepare an answer yourself and to share it with the students after they have responded. "Does believing in Jesus make any difference in your life?" is a good follow-up question.

Item #4: Have several junior highers share their completed sentences.

To Close the Session:

Share with your students what Christ means to you. If you can, stress what knowing Christ has done for your life. An appropriate scripture is John 9:25: "All I know is this — once I was blind and now I see!" It isn't as important to define Christ as it is to let Christ change our lives. The only way we can understand Christ is to encounter Him, to experience His power in our lives.

Help your students think of Christ as a friend, someone who will stay close to them and to whom they can always take their problems. Invite them to enter into a personal relationship with Jesus.

Outside Activities:

Undertake a detailed study of the life of Christ with your students.

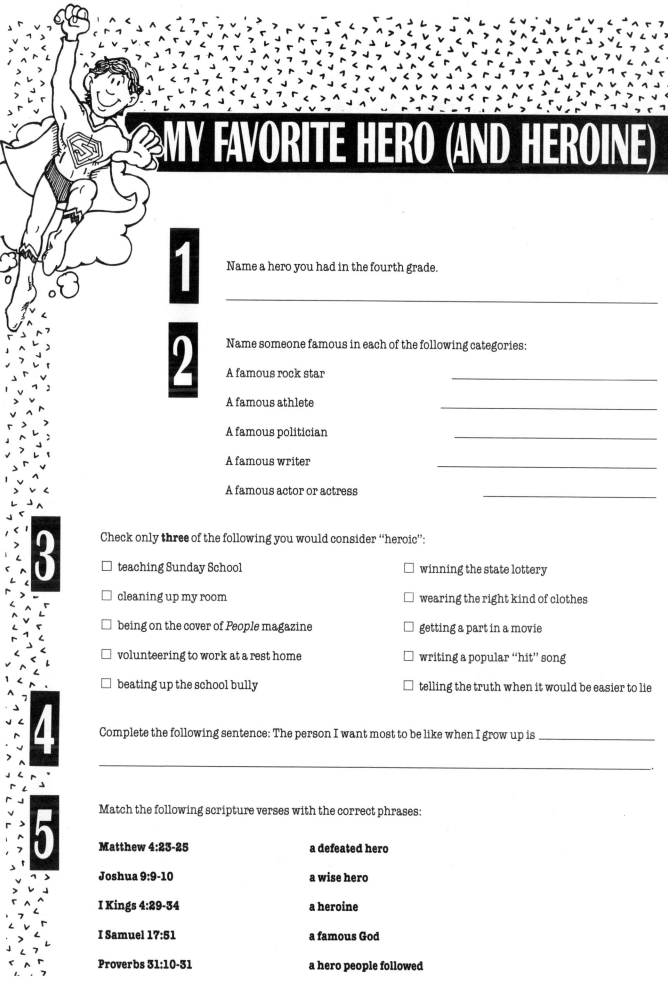

MY FAVORITE HERO (AND HEROINE)

1 Name a hero you had in the fourth grade.

_____

2 Name someone famous in each of the following categories:

A famous rock star _____

A famous athlete _____

A famous politician _____

A famous writer _____

A famous actor or actress _____

3 Check only **three** of the following you would consider "heroic":

☐ teaching Sunday School   ☐ winning the state lottery

☐ cleaning up my room   ☐ wearing the right kind of clothes

☐ being on the cover of _People_ magazine   ☐ getting a part in a movie

☐ volunteering to work at a rest home   ☐ writing a popular "hit" song

☐ beating up the school bully   ☐ telling the truth when it would be easier to lie

4 Complete the following sentence: The person I want most to be like when I grow up is _____

_____.

5 Match the following scripture verses with the correct phrases:

Matthew 4:23-25	**a defeated hero**
Joshua 9:9-10	**a wise hero**
I Kings 4:29-34	**a heroine**
I Samuel 17:51	**a famous God**
Proverbs 31:10-31	**a hero people followed**

MY FAVORITE HERO (AND HEROINE)

Topic: Heroes

Purpose of this Session:

Too many of today's heroes and heroines are creations of media hype. They are celebrities shaped by television, movies and videos. They are anything from rock stars to television personalities. But their moral behavior is not the role model we want our children to emulate. This TalkSheet will help you discuss what a hero really is.

To Introduce the Topic:

A crazy, fun way to begin this session is to rent a Superman costume (or another super-hero get-up, such as Mighty Mouse or Batman) and wear it to the meeting. You might wish to prepare a skit with a "villian", a "heroine" — the damsel in distress; then the superhero (you) dashes into the room to save the day. There are numerous appropriate skits ("The Spontaneous Melodrama") in the book *The Greatest Skits on Earth* by Wayne Rice and Mike Yaconelli (Youth Specialties/Zondervan, 1986)

A less dramatic way to begin is to display several magazines which feature prominent people on their covers. Ask the students to rate these featured personalities according to their "hero potential".

The Discussion:

Item #1: Ask a few students to name the heroes they remember from the fourth grade. See how many are still heroes. Ask the students if they know why the people were important to them.

Item #2: Discuss the difference between a famous person today — known as a celebrity — and a hero or heroine. A celebrity is a creation of media publicity. Heroes earn their titles and we often reflect on the merits of what they have done. Heroes take moral positions and live by exemplary standards. The emphasis on celebrities has detracted from our sense of right and wrong because celebrity status is often achieved by the immoral.

Item #3: Point out heroic deeds do not always bring fame. Fame has nothing to do with morality today. Instead, it deals with what is popular and trendy. Help the students see that a heroic act may be something as insignificant as "cleaning up your room", because it is an act of discipline, obedience and respect.

Item #4: Ask the students to share the people they chose. Many will choose Jesus or their parents. This is a good time to talk about their role-models. Parents and Jesus are often very good choices. A good follow-up question is, "What can you do to become more like the person you chose?"

Item #5: As you go over these Biblical passages, discuss the many heroes and heroines in the Bible and what caused each to be heroic.

To Close the Session:

Everyone needs a hero, but we should choose our heroes wisely. The apostle Paul said, "Imitate me." He wasn't boasting. He was saying, "I'll be your hero. You need a hero who acts as Jesus wants him to do. Imitate me as I imitate Christ" (Phil. 3:17). Don't model yourself after anyone who does not reflect the values and high standards of the Christian faith.

Challenge your students not only to choose their heroes carefully but also to strive to do the heroic deed. Many may think they are "nobodies", but you can encourage them to believe they can do great things for the kingdom of God. "I can do all things through Christ who gives me strength", wrote Paul (Phil. 4:13). Let the group members know there are younger Christians looking up to them.

Outside Activities:

1. Have the students poll their friends to find out who they consider heroes and heroines, then have them report their findings.

2. Ask the students to find out what heroes and heroines their parents had when they were young, and report the following week.

What, Me Worry?

1 Mark an **"X"** next to all the things on the following list you worry about from time to time. Put a star beside those you have worried about recently.

_____ what others think of me   _____ my body changing
_____ my grades   _____ sex
_____ what high school will be like   _____ family fights
_____ how I look   _____ my relationship with God
_____ nuclear war   _____ not having enough money
_____ parents divorcing   _____ world problems
_____ making friends   _____ other: _____

2 Complete this sentence: The more I worry about something . . .

_____ the worse it becomes   _____ the more I realize it doesn't change a thing

_____ the better it becomes   _____ the worse it gets in my mind

3 What would you say to a friend who was worried about:

a. Their parents getting a divorce. _____
_____

b. Failing a class. _____
_____

c. A bad haircut. _____
_____

d. Getting caught cheating on a test. _____
_____

4 How can a person get rid of worry? Write your answer:

_____
_____
_____
_____

5 Read the following verses and summarize each in five words or less:

1 Peter 5:7 _____

Philippians 4:6-7 _____

Romans 8:28 _____

WHAT, ME WORRY?

Topic: Worry

Purpose of this Session:

Adolescents worry a great deal. They worry about their looks, their relationships, and their future. Because of an increased amount of stress and tension placed upon them by modern lifestyles, the present generation may have more to worry about than any other has had. This TalkSheet will help your group talk about their worries and insecurities and how their faith in Christ can be a positive force in dealing with them.

To Introduce the Session:

Play a game called "Worries Charades". Either you or someone you choose acts out the different worries you have pre-selected. The rest of the group tries to guess what kind of worry is being portrayed. Keep the worries humorous. Some possibilities: body odor, a pimple on the nose, flunking a math test, not knowing how to kiss, fly is open, can't get to sleep, going to the dentist, passing gas.

The Discussion:

Item #1: Begin by talking about some of the things that worried you as a teenager. Then let the students share things that worry them the most. Act as moderator and use effective listening. You will gain valuable insight into their lives.

Item #2: Your students will probably find a logical reason to find each answer correct. Point out that most of the time, worrying doesn't do anything to improve a situation. Only when worry leads to positive action is it worthwhile.

Item #3: Have the students share their advice with the others. You may wish to role-play the situations, with one student acting the worrier and the other giving advice.

Item #4: Brainstorm different solutions to worrying. List others on the board for everyone to see. Define the difference between worrying which doesn't change things and concern, which motivates change. Young people need to understand worrying is a waste of invested emotional energy. Concern uses this energy to solve the problem.

Item #5: After studying the scriptures, have the students choose one to memorize. They can then repeat the scripture to themselves when they next begin to worry about something.

To Close the Session:

The English word "worry" comes from a German word *"wurgen"*, meaning "to choke". Worry is mental strangulation and can kill.

It is normal and healthy to have worries, but it is destructive, self-defeating and useless to worry about things over which you have no control. If you can control an outcome of a "worry", then you can do something about it in a positive way.

Help your students realize Christians need not worry about what has happened in the past, nor about what is to happen in the future. Both are in God's hands. We are forgiven the past and God is in control of the future. Jesus came to give us inner peace and a positive outlook on life. Jesus says to us, "Do not worry, little flock" (Matthew 6).

Tell the group one of the best ways to get rid of worry is to talk about it with someone else — a friend, a parent, another respected adult — someone who is willing to listen. Let them know you are available to listen and help. Sometimes all a person needs to feel more secure about something is to be able to dump their worries on someone else.

Outside Activities:

The greatest way to forget your own troubles is to help someone else. Have your youth group plan a Christian service project, such as visiting a retirement home.

YOU MAKE ME SO MAD

a. Someone calls you a dirty name.
b. Your parents put you on restriction.
c. You flunk a test.
d. You have to do two hours of homework.
e. Someone steals your bike.
f. You are in a bad mood when your mom asks you to help with the dishes.
g. Someone bullies you.
h. A friend talks about you behind your back.
i. Your parents blame you for something you didn't do.
j. You have lost your allowance.

 Circle three from the situations listed to the right that would make you really mad:

2 Complete the following sentences:

When my mom gets mad, she _____

When my dad gets mad, he _____

When I get mad, I _____

3 Darrin is standing patiently in the cafeteria line at lunch time. Two guys push their way into the line, cutting in front of Darrin. He is shoved off balance, falls down, and loses his place in line.

How would you feel if you were Darrin? _____

What would you do if you were Darrin? _____

4 YES or NO?

	YES	NO
a. I have the right to be angry with someone who hurts me.	☐	☐
b. People who lose their temper are immature.	☐	☐
c. Anger is a sin.	☐	☐
d. Christians should show anger differently from non-Christians.	☐	☐
e. Don't get mad, get even.	☐	☐

5 Choose one of the following scriptures to rewrite in your own words:

Proverbs 14:17   **Proverbs 15:1**   **Ephesians 4:26-27**

_____

_____

_____

_____

_____

_____

YOU MAKE ME SO MAD

Topic: Anger

Purpose of this Session:

Anger is a difficult emotion for most people to handle, especially adolescents. A proverb states, "Anger, like fire, finally dies out — but not before it leaves a path of destruction." Young people experience anger frequently as they discover the world is not as ideal as they would like. But they haven't yet learned how to handle anger. This TalkSheet gives your group a chance to study anger and decide how a Christian should handle it.

To Introduce the Topic:

Ask for a volunteer actor to help you introduce this session. Before the meeting, have him or her "bug" you incessantly. During the opening of the meeting, the music, the announcements, games, etc., he/she will annoy you constantly and disrupt the meeting. Just before the discussion begins, pretend you have lost your patience and blow your top. Tell the student actor to get out and never come back, in no uncertain terms. Then let the group in on the ruse and announce you are going to talk about anger.

The Discussion:

Item #1: Allow enough time for the students to share the items they circled. Explain they can rise above certain circumstances and choose not to get angry. They do not have to let other people or circumstances make them mad.

Item #2: Oftentimes, we handle anger the same way our parents do. This item may help your students understand their own reactions. Let individuals talk about the different ways in which they and their parents handle anger.

Item #3: You can use this "Tension Getter" to role-play a true-to-life situation with the group. Ask the students to think of their own frustrating situations to solve and discuss.

Item #4: Many young people have difficulty expressing anger. They either hold it inside or let it out in destructive ways. Some may feel anger is a sin. It is not. It is an emotional reaction. Christ told us to be happy but not to sin. Anger is not the problem. It is what we do with the anger that counts. Communicate, through a discussion of these items, that anger is a normal emotion all of us have. We each need to learn appropriate ways to handle that anger.

Item #5: Ask several students to share their paraphrased scriptures and to try to apply them to their own lives.

To Close the Session:

Normal Vincent Peale said, "The next time you feel the surge of anger, say to yourself, 'Is this really worth what it's going to do to me and another, emotionally? I will make a fool of myself. I may hurt someone I love, or I might lose a friend.'"

Challenge your group members to express their anger in positive, constructive ways. Encourage them to "delay" their temper until they've had a chance to cool off. If they are still having difficulty handling anger, have them role-play pertinent situations and responses. Assure them their angry feelings are not sinful. It is their reaction that is important and within their control.

Outside Activities:

1. Have the students cut out newspaper articles during the coming week, illustrating anger. Debrief the articles by talking about why there is so much anger in our society and how they can become Christian peacemakers.

2. Have several students create a bulletin board or poster related to anger. Let them share what they have learned.

3. Ask the members to bring a rock song that expresses anger or rebellion. Play the song, then talk about why the anger was there and what could be done about it.

PARENTS ARE PEOPLE, TOO

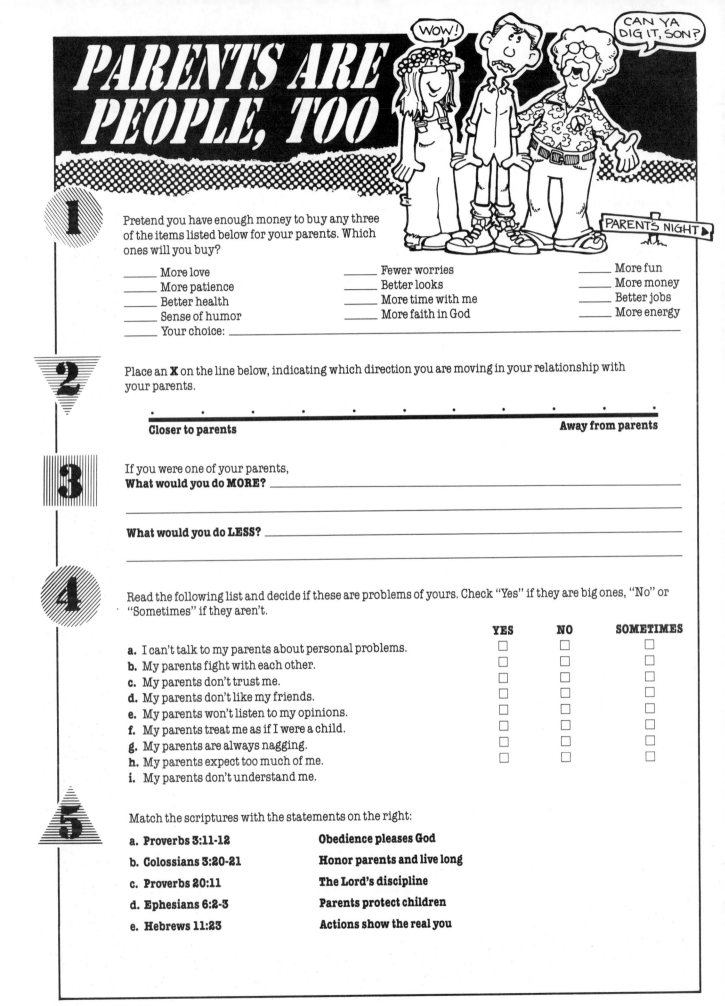

1 Pretend you have enough money to buy any three of the items listed below for your parents. Which ones will you buy?

_____ More love
_____ More patience
_____ Better health
_____ Sense of humor
_____ Your choice: _____

_____ Fewer worries
_____ Better looks
_____ More time with me
_____ More faith in God

_____ More fun
_____ More money
_____ Better jobs
_____ More energy

2 Place an **X** on the line below, indicating which direction you are moving in your relationship with your parents.

Closer to parents   **Away from parents**

3 If you were one of your parents,
What would you do MORE? _____

_____

What would you do LESS? _____

_____

4 Read the following list and decide if these are problems of yours. Check "Yes" if they are big ones, "No" or "Sometimes" if they aren't.

	YES	NO	SOMETIMES
a. I can't talk to my parents about personal problems.	☐	☐	☐
b. My parents fight with each other.	☐	☐	☐
c. My parents don't trust me.	☐	☐	☐
d. My parents don't like my friends.	☐	☐	☐
e. My parents won't listen to my opinions.	☐	☐	☐
f. My parents treat me as if I were a child.	☐	☐	☐
g. My parents are always nagging.	☐	☐	☐
h. My parents expect too much of me.	☐	☐	☐
i. My parents don't understand me.			

5 Match the scriptures with the statements on the right:

a. Proverbs 3:11-12   **Obedience pleases God**

b. Colossians 3:20-21   **Honor parents and live long**

c. Proverbs 20:11   **The Lord's discipline**

d. Ephesians 6:2-3   **Parents protect children**

e. Hebrews 11:23   **Actions show the real you**

Date Used: _____

Group: _____

PARENTS ARE PEOPLE, TOO

Topic: Parents

Purpose of this Session:

As children become adolescents, they begin to have an identity of their own. They begin to grow away from their parents and strive for independence. This always causes a certain amount of difficulty in the home. To the parents, the teenager seems rebellious and distant; to the youngster, the parents seem old-fashioned and overly strict. This TalkSheet is designed to help you discuss parent-teen relationships with your students in a constructive and positive way.

To Introduce the Topic:

Have the students create skits about parental behavior. Divide them into small groups and ask each group to produce their own skit, with parent-teen relationships as the theme. Debrief the skits when all have performed. Talk about what they learned, good and bad, from the skits.

Another good lead-in is to have the students think of some "famous parents" they would like to have as their own (from TV sitcoms, etc.) and then explain why.

The Discussion:

Item #1: This item will allow the students to think in terms of what they believe their parents need the most. It will also give you some clues as to what they value the most. Let volunteers share their choices.

Item #2: Allow discussion about where the young people think their relationships with their parents are going. Once they have shared, brainstorm different ways in which they can improve their relationships with their parents.

Item #3: Emphasize the positive with this item. Encourage thinking of the good things the students' parents do, with them and for them. Don't let this turn into a gripe session.

Item #4: Rather than asking the students to share on this one, ask them to decide if those marked "yes" and "sometimes" are those that either (a) can't be changed, so should be accepted, (b) they can change, or (c) they need help with. Brainstorm ideas with the group about the whole list — how to overcome each problem or improve each situation. Be certain those that want help get it, either from yourself, your pastor, other church parents, concerned parents, or a qualified counselor. Don't assume those who are having trouble are somehow getting help. They probably are not. You can provide a great ministry to their lives by referring them to appropriate help.

Item #5: Read the scriptures and ask the students how they can be applied to their own home situation.

To Close the Session:

Your youth group needs to be encouraged to "hang in there" with their parents. Keep your closing comments affirmative and upbeat. They need to hear they can make it with their parents, with God's help.

Emphasize the fact that their parents are not perfect, but they are the only parents they have. God gave us our parents and we need to be thankful for them. Encourage your students to talk to their parents more often and to try and see their point of view as often as they can.

Remind the group God has commanded us to honor and obey our parents (Exodus 20:12). This is one of the Ten Commandments. It comes with a promise. We won't regret loving and honoring our parents.

It would be appropriate to close with a prayer for everyone's parents.

Outside Activities:

1. Have your young people write a letter to their parents. They should include several "thank-you's" and an "I love you". Some have difficulty telling their parents they love them. A letter can make this easier.

2. Give your students a "parents quiz" which they must take during the week. Include questions about their parents which they can answer only by talking to them, such as: How old were your parents when they first started dating? What were their majors in college? What is their biggest problem? How did they celebrate their first anniversary? etc.

HUNGER HURTS

1 What is your favorite food? _____

_____

2 Complete the sentences below by checking the ending that is appropriate for you:

I eat . . .

_____ one meal a day

_____ two meals a day

_____ three meals a day

_____ more than three meals a day

_____ three meals a day, plus snacks

_____ whenever I feel hungry

I eat . . .

_____ less than the average person my age

_____ more than the average person my age

_____ about the same as the average person my age

I eat . . .

_____ only what I know is good for me

_____ anything that tastes good

_____ mostly junk food

_____ whatever my family eats

When I am hungry . . .

_____ I wait until the next meal

_____ I have a snack

_____ I go crazy!

3 Do you AGREE or DISAGREE?

	AGREE	DISAGREE
a. There are no hungry people in America.	☐	☐
b. It is their own fault if some people are hungry.	☐	☐
c. It is God's will for some people of the world to be hungry.	☐	☐
d. One should not eat just for pleasure.	☐	☐
e. It is a sin to overeat.	☐	☐
f. There is nothing I can do to help the hungry people of the world.	☐	☐

4 Match the scriptures with the correct statements:

Luke 16:19-26   **poor always around**

Acts 11:28-30   **rich man and Lazarus**

John 12:8   **Christians help others**

Deuteronomy 14:28-29   **reward for helping poor**

Matthew 25:34-36   **God's command to help**

HUNGER HURTS

Topic: World Hunger

Purpose of this Session:

For most young people, world hunger seems remote and unreal. They sometimes hear about it, or see pictures of starving people, but they don't really identify with the victims of world hunger, who could be people like themselves who enjoy hamburgers and pizza. This TalkSheet was designed to help our young people think about their own eating habits in light of world hunger and to see how their faith affects their lifestyle decisions.

To Introduce the Topic:

An effective way to get the group's attentions for this discussion is to bring a delicious selection of food to the meeting and eat it in front of them. While you are eating, make some announcements, or talk about something, but keep eating and say, "I didn't have time to eat before the meeting, and I hope you don't mind my eating in front of you. . ." If the food you are eating is really appealing (such as a nice, hot pizza), they will probably go nuts watching you eat. You might be able to have a pizza delivered just as the meeting begins.

Debrief the experience by asking how they felt while watching you eat, smelling the food, etc. Introduce the topic "Hunger Hurts" and distribute the TalkSheets.

There are also many excellent films, posters and slide presentations available free or at a very low cost from organizations such as World Vision or Compassion International which you could order.

The Discussion:

Item #1: This forces the students to think about the kinds of foods they enjoy eating the most. Without being judgmental or trying to make them feel guilty, point out the simple truth that in many countries, young people have no choice about what they eat. Most have never tasted the wonderful variety of foods available to us.

Item #2: Junior high students are a hungry bunch. Their bodies are in a state of constant growth and need plenty of nourishment for healthy development. Let them share their responses with the group. Point out how important food is to them as well as to young people around the world.

Item #3: Go over each statement. Item "b" is one to study carefully because many adults as well as young people believe the hungry and the poor are to blame for their condition. Be sensitive to the ones in your group who are overweight when looking at "d" and "e". Their self-esteem is already suffering. Some may bring up dieting at this point. Talk about dieting because many young people of today have problems in that area. Far too much emphasis has been put upon dieting and being thin. Anorexia nervosa is a growing problem among teens. Try to generate specific responses to "f". Help them see they can be involved in helping feed the hungry. End this discussion by agreeing upon one specific thing the group can do to help fight world hunger.

Item #4: Ask the students to read the passages and match them up correctly. Discuss the scriptures one at a time and ask them to try to apply their messages to their own lives.

To Close the Session:

Help the students understand the food they have to eat — and take for granted — is a gift from God. We should always thank God for our food and pray others around the world also have enough to eat.

Let them know they can actually make a difference. Just because they cannot go to Ethiopia doesn't mean they cannot help provide food for the starving there. Tell the story of the "Feeding of the 5000" in which a small boy gave his lunch to Jesus and Jesus used his gift to feed a multitude. In the same way, we can give a small amount to Jesus, through organizations Jesus is using to feed the hungry, and our gift will be multiplied.

Instigate a group fund raising activity, such as a Saturday afternoon car wash at a shopping center, for a Christian relief agency. End the session with a prayer for the hungry people of the world.

Outside Activities:

Follow through on the hunger project your group decides to undertake. For more good ideas, consult the book *Ideas for Social Action* by Anthony Campolo (Youth Specialties/Zondervan, 1983).

Honestly

1 Which of the following do you consider the most honest?
(Write "HP" next to the "Honest People".)

_____ The President of the United States
_____ A door-to-door salesman
_____ A minister
_____ A celebrity in a television commercial
_____ Your parents
_____ Your best friend
_____ A school teacher
_____ A rock star
_____ A police officer
_____ You

2 Try to answer this question: **What is a "white lie?"**

_____
_____
_____

3 Most would say the following are dishonest statements. Rank them from 1 to 6, with 1 being the MOST dishonest and 6 being the LEAST.

_____ Lying to parents in order to get permission to go out.

_____ Cheating on a test.

_____ Keeping the money when a cashier gives you too much change.

_____ Borrowing something and not returning it.

_____ Spreading a rumor when it's not true.

_____ Shoplifting.

_____ Giving a fake excuse to a teacher.

_____ Saying "I forgot", when you really didn't.

4 Natalie lied to her parents about where she spent the afternoon. She knew if she told her parents the truth, they would be disappointed and angry. Her parents believed her and nothing more was said.

What do you think of Natalie's actions? _____

_____

What would you do if you were Natalie? _____

_____

5 Decide which of the following scriptures are examples of honesty and which are examples of dishonesty.

Acts 5:1-2	I Samuel 12:1-5	2 Corinthians 8:19-21
Genesis 12:10-13	Amos 8:4-5	Luke 19:5-8

HONESTLY

Topic: Honesty

Purpose of this Session:

It is important to discuss honesty with young people because during adolescence, dishonesty becomes more than just "telling lies". Children tell fibs and lie to get what they want, but adolescents begin to wrestle with the issue of honesty as a *value*. They must decide whether or not they will choose to be a completely honest person.

To Introduce the Topic:

A good lead-in is to play the game "Whopper". Have the students write three statements about themselves, two of which are true and one of which is not. The rest of the group members try to guess which of the three is a lie. If the students choose two truths that *sound* like lies and a lie that sounds plausible, they will be successful at fooling the group.

Another idea is to conduct a "lying contest". Have a contest to find out who can tell the biggest lie. After each student has told his fib, vote on the best "tall tale". Give a prize to the winner, or announce you will present a new car to the owner, then later admit *you* lied.

The Discussion:

Item #1: The main focus of this item is "trust". Who do we trust to tell us the truth? If there are those on the list the students perceive as dishonest, ask them why. It will probably be due to a past experience with dishonesty. Trust takes time to develop and we destroy it when we are dishonest with each other.

Item #2: Allow enough time for the group to share and discuss their opinions. You may want to discuss "white" and "black" lies, asking the students to give examples of each and why they feel they are permissable lies or not. You may want to discuss the kind of lies that are considered "good" — such as telling someone they look nice when they don't, or lying to protect a friend from harm. Is this right or wrong?

Item #3: Ask the students to share their rankings and to give reasons for their choices. There may be considerable difference of opinion here, so allow time for debate.

Item #4: This "Tension Getter" will give you a true-to-life situation to discuss with the students. Ask them to decide what Natalie should have done and what she should do now. Ask them to consider all the possible consequences of this kind of dishonesty. Even though Natalie "got away with it", there is no way of knowing what might happen as a result. On the other hand, everyone knows the result of being completely honest.

Item #5: These scriptures examine different aspects of honesty. Discuss each one as you study what God has to say about honesty.

To Close the Sesssion:

Summarize what has been discussed. Focus some of your concluding remarks on the consequences of honesty and dishonesty. Being dishonest is like playing with dynamite. It can blow up in your face. Help the students understand one lie tends to lead to another. "Oh what a tangled web we weave, when first we practice to deceive!" Being consistently guilty of misrepresentation can destroy your reputation and your sense of self-worth. Being consistently guilty of misrepresentation can destroy your reputation and your sense of self-worth. One of the key characteristics of a Christian is honesty and being trustworthy. Jesus said "I am the truth" and we need to imitate Christ by being truthful people. Remind your students God will forgive them for past untruths.

Outside Activities:

Invite the students' parents to a youth group meeting for a panel discussion on honesty. Have them share instances when they were not completely truthful as teenagers, and what happened as a result. Insist on complete honesty! Have them discuss how they deal with dishonesty now, at home or at work.

THE HEAT IS ON

1 Which of the following are common problems with your age group? (Check the most three most prevalent.)

_____ Getting bad grades.   _____ Sex problems.
_____ Health problems.   _____ Not looking good enough.
_____ Not having enough friends.   _____ Not having enough time.
_____ Being bored.   _____ Being picked up after school.
_____ Not having enough money.   _____ Family problems.
_____ Having parents that are too strict.

2 Complete the following sentence: **If I could change one thing about my life, it would be . . .**

_____

_____

_____

3 I am having . . . _____ (check one of the phrases below) _____ . . . as most people my age.

_____ **more problems**
_____ **less problems**
_____ **about the same number of problems**

4 **You be the judge.** How serious are each of the following problems in your life?

	BIG PROBLEM	LITTLE PROBLEM	NO PROBLEM
a. I feel lonely most of the time.	☐	☐	☐
b. I feel far away from God.	☐	☐	☐
c. My parents don't understand me.	☐	☐	☐
d. I feel depressed a lot of the time.	☐	☐	☐
e. Church is boring.	☐	☐	☐
f. I don't feel good about myself.	☐	☐	☐
g. My teachers don't like me.	☐	☐	☐
h. I get myself in trouble a lot of the time.	☐	☐	☐

5 Read the following scriptures and write out what you think each has to say about problems.

Proverbs _____

_____

1 Thessalonians 5:18 _____

_____

Corinthians 1:3-5 _____

_____

_____

THE HEAT IS ON

Topic: Problems of junior high students

Purpose of this Session:

Each stage of life presents its own unique set of problems. Early adolescence is no exception. Unlike adults, young people at this stage of life lack the experience and resources adults have in dealing with problems. They often feel alone and ill-equipped to handle them. This TalkSheet will give you an opportunity to talk about common problems, concerns, and frustrations of the junior high school years, and how to solve them.

To Introduce this Session:

Have everyone write their biggest problem on a sheet of paper. This could be done as a "Letter to Ann Landers" or a "Dear Abby" letter. Collect and screen the problems. Choose several to solve. Ask for volunteers to pretend the problems are theirs. Ask them to read the problems and present them to the group for a solution. Encourage the use of scripture where appropriate. The person with the problem gets help without revealing he or she is the troubled one. You also have a great lead-in for discussing problems.

The Discussion:

Item #1: Go through this list and ask for a show of hands on each of the problems. Decide which is the biggest. Ask if there are other big problems that are not listed, common to their age group.

Item #2: Make a master list of all the changes your students would like. Decide which they have control over and which they do not. Explore why these changes are desirable. Reinforce the idea that God accepts us the way we are and not the way we think we ought to be. The key to a positive self-image is accepting ourselves the same way God accepts us.

Item #3: Ask the students how they would answer for minority youth, handicapped youth, Third World youth, etc. Let them see they are not the only ones with problems.

Item #4: With each of these problems, brainstorm a solution to each. This will give your students some good practice in problem solving. You may also wish to go back to Item #1 and discuss solutions to the problems identified there.

Item #5: These scriptures look at problems from different perspectives. Ask several student to read what they have written.

To Close the Session:

The story of David and Goliath is appropriate for the closing of this session. Goliath presented a big problem for David. There were people who probably said to David, "David, that giant is so big, there's no way you can win!" But David's attitude as he loaded his sling was, "No, the giant is so big, there's no way I can miss!" Even the biggest problem can become an opportunity to grow and become a winner.

Reassure your students that problems are normal, even expected. Let your group know you are available to talk about their problems. Encourage them to discuss their problems with their parents. If this is impossible, suggest another trustworthy adult like yourself, the pastor, or school counselor. Challenge them to view the problems from God's perspective. Challenge them to take their difficulties to God.

Outside Activities:

1. Have adult leaders schedule appointments with each of your students to discuss some of the tough problems they are facing. Do this on a voluntary basis.

2. Instigate a service project that focuses on the problems of others.

3. Have the students cut out newspaper articles that deal with problems of other people. Discuss what is learned from the project. This will help them move away from their egocentric point of view.

YOUTH GROUP

1 Complete this sentence: The best thing about this youth group is _____
_____
_____
_____
_____
_____

2 Circle one of the words listed below that best describes this youth group:

struggling	**loving**	**dead**	**fun**	**alive**
great	**boring**		**growing**	**average**

3 If you could change one thing about this youth group to make it better, what would you change? _____
_____
_____
_____
_____
_____

4 Your opinion, please! **!**=THAT'S RIGHT! **?**=SOMETIMES **X**=NO WAY!

a. Our youth group has good leaders. _____

b. I feel like I'm an integral part of this youth group. _____

c. I attend youth group meetings mostly because my parents make me. _____

d. This youth group is important to me. _____

e. I feel close to God because of this youth group. _____

f. I have a lot of good friends in this youth group. _____

g. What we do in the youth group helps me. _____

h. I feel like I can invite my friends to this youth group. _____

5 Read **Ephesians 4:1-6**, then write a postcard to your youth group explaining what you have learned and how it can improve the youth group.

Dear Youth Group:

_____
_____
_____
_____
_____
_____
_____

Date Used: _____

Group: _____

MY YOUTH GROUP

Topic: Evaluation of your youth group

Purpose of this Session:

Young people often take their youth group for granted. When it's going great, they enjoy it. When tough times come, they complain. This session gives you and your group the opportunity to assess the status of the group in a positive way. You can also use this TalkSheet with the leaders of the group as a planning tool.

To Introduce the Topic:

There are several approaches appropriate for talking about the health and condition of your youth group. Whichever you choose, keep the theme upbeat and affirmative. Don't let this turn into a "gripe session". Let the students talk about other groups they have visited or of which they have been members. This will illustrate that no group is perfect.

Another lead-in would be to allow the students to imitate adults leading a youth group function. This can be hilarious and you may learn a thing or two about yourself. Another way would be to have the adult leaders share what the group means to them.

The Discussion:

Item #1: This incomplete sentence begins things on a positive note. State that you hope to keep the discussion positive and upbeat. Interrupt the discussion if it becomes too negative or full of put-downs.

Item #2: Ask the students to share the words they circled. Ask if they can think of any additional words to describe the youth group.

Item #3: Allow the students to share their criticisms but in a constuctive way. Remind them the purpose of this is to improve the group, not destroy it.

Item #4: Again, keep this exercise as positive as possible. It is imperative this session doesn't disintegrate into a gripe session. Ask volunteers to share their responses of the questions, one at a time, or to make comments.

Item #5: Have the students share ways they feel the group could improve. You may want to collect and peruse the TalkSheets to better find out how they really feel about the group. Tell them in advance not to put their names on the TalkSheets.

To Close the Session:

Close with a positive affirmation of each person in the group. Let them know they are important to the group and that their comments and concerns will be taken seriously. This would be a good time to invite them to take a more active part in the group activities and to get involved. Close with an appropriate prayer for the youth group and its leaders.

Outside Activities:

Have a planning session in which the students help brainstorm ideas for activities and programs for the coming year. A good resource to use for this is *The Youth Group Planning Calendar* by David Lynn (Youth Specialties, 1224 Greenfield Dr., El Cajon, CA 92021.)

Are You Talking About Me?

1

Compared to others your age, how would you rate yourself?

Your looks:

_____ Above average

_____ Average

_____ Below average

Your intellect:

_____ Above average

_____ Average

_____ Below average

Your personality:

_____ Above average

_____ Average

_____ Below average

Your popularity:

_____ Above average

_____ Average

_____ Below average

2

Make a list of the things you are proud of about yourself: _____

_____

_____

_____

_____

_____

_____

3

Read each of the following statements, then check "That's Me" or "That's Not Me":

	THAT'S ME	THAT'S NOT ME
a. I like the way I look.	☐	☐
b. I live my life the way I think others want me to live it.	☐	☐
c. Sometimes I wish I were someone else.	☐	☐
d. I don't think I am normal.	☐	☐
e. I sometimes do things I know I shouldn't, in order to be accepted.	☐	☐
f. I believe God loves me just the way I am.	☐	☐
g. When I meet new people, I worry they may not like me the way I am.	☐	☐

4

The following is a paraphrase of Psalm 139:13-18. Write your name in the blanks, then read it to yourself. Think about how important you are in God's eyes.

God, you created all the complex parts of my body while I was still inside my mother. Thank you, Lord, for creating me, _____ (your name). I know you cared when you made me. While my bones were still forming, before anyone else knew who I was, you knew I, _____, was alive. You could see who I was even before I was born, and you had already planned my days on earth before I lived any one of them. You think about me all of the time. You love me so much. Every minute, even when I get up in the morning, you are thinking about me.

ARE YOU TALKING ABOUT ME?

Topic: Self-image / self-esteem

Purpose of this Session:

Self-esteem is of utmost importance to adolescents. They worry about how they look, how they act, and whether or not they will be accepted and liked. This TalkSheet gives your group the opportunity to discuss self-image and self-esteem and will give you a chance to affirm your students and assure them they are okay.

To Introduce the Session:

Have the students pin a piece of paper on each other's backs. Have everyone write something they like about each other on the papers. Allow enough time for each person to read their papers and discuss how they feel.

The Discussion:

Item #1: Do not ask the students to reveal their answers to this item. Instead, have them think about their answers and what they have learned about themselves. How adolescents feel about themselves is often based on how they think others feel about them. The impressions revealed by this exercise are usually the result of others' perceptions, rather than a realistic appraisal. State that God views them from a different perspective than their peers do. They need to know they have some control over how they see themselves, rather than allowing others' opinions to control their self-esteem.

Item #2: This is designed to accentuate the positive. Ask the students to share, voluntarily, the traits they are proud of. Or, have them share what they would be proud of, if *they were the person on their right.* Try to get the focus on personal qualities and accomplishments.

Item #3: You may wish to make this a more general discussion. Focus on an imaginary teenager and how he/she might feel. Your students might open up more if you share how you felt about yourself when you were a teenager.

Item #4: This Psalm has been paraphrased to emphasize the fact that God loves each person, for themselves. Have the group read the scripture aloud, then lead a discussion about what it means to their feelings of self-esteem.

To Close the Session:

Young people need to realize feelings of inadequacy are normal. Even high achievers who seem to be self-confident have feelings of inadequacy and fears of failure. Challenge your students to begin seeing themselves as God sees them. They are children of God, created in the image of God. They can control their own self-esteem rather than let the opinion of others affect it.

Emphasize they have the potential to become all they want to become — if they acknowledge God's power in their lives and allow Him to take control. Biblical examples include Moses (who had a speech impediment) and Paul (who apparently was not very handsome and had a "thorn in the flesh".) If we keep putting ourselves down, God cannot use us.

Sometimes we have low self-images because we are overly preoccupied with ourselves. The media caters to this by making us feel inferior and by telling us our lives are not as exciting and glamourous as those of celebrities. This is a trap. The best way to stop feeling sorry for our lot in life is to cease being self-centered and to put others first.

God created us in His image. He loves us, cares about us, and even died for us. He loves us as we are, not as we "ought to be".

Outside Activities:

1. Have your students write affirming notes to each other (anonymously) and mail them during the week. Assign names making sure no one is left out. Discuss these notes at the next meeting.

2. Have the students keep a journal for a week, noting when they felt inadequate and discouraged. At the next meeting, share what they learned from the experience.

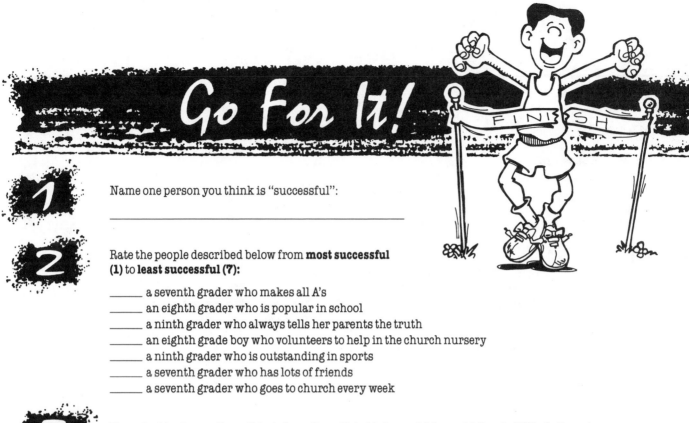

Go For It!

1 Name one person you think is "successful":

_____

2 Rate the people described below from **most successful (1)** to **least successful (7):**

_____ a seventh grader who makes all A's

_____ an eighth grader who is popular in school

_____ a ninth grader who always tells her parents the truth

_____ an eighth grade boy who volunteers to help in the church nursery

_____ a ninth grader who is outstanding in sports

_____ a seventh grader who has lots of friends

_____ a seventh grader who goes to church every week

3 If you had to give up three things from those listed below, which would they be? (Circle three.)

bike   TV   church   friends   allowance   parents

4 Answer each of the following questions by circling one of the three choices.

a. How popular do you want to be?
VERY POPULAR
SOMEWHAT POPULAR
NOT POPULAR AT ALL

b. How rich do you want to be?
BIG BUCKS
COMFORTABLE
ENOUGH TO GET BY

c. Who is the more successful?
MILLIONAIRE
ROCK STAR
PRO ATHLETE
MISSIONARY

d. Which would you rather be?
SMART
GOOD
POWERFUL

e. What kind of life do you want?
EXCITING
SPIRITUAL
COMFORTABLE

f. How do you want others to see you?
LOSER
WINNER
ORDINARY

5 Read each of the Bible verses and finish the sentences accordingly.

The world says focus on yourself, but the Bible says . . .

(Matthew 10:39) _____

The world says it has a lot to offer you, but the Bible says . . .

(1 John 2:15-17) _____

The world says it loves you, but the Bible says . . .

(John 15:18-21) _____

GO FOR IT!

Topic: Success

Purpose of this Session:

Success is a buzz-word of modern culture. Our young people are being conditioned to seek only success and the status symbols that go along with it. Adults consider money, prestige, and power synonymous with success. Our children are no different. They focus on having the right clothes, the right friends, being seen with the "in crowd", etc. This TalkSheet was designed to examine the real meaning of success in light of the Christian faith.

To Introduce the Topic:

Many times young people do not believe they are as success-oriented as adults. To illustrate how they are focused on success and to introduce the topic, have them create a master list of things, titles or activities that give a teenager status with his or her peers. They may list things like designer clothing, being a member of a certain group, etc. Create the list on a chalkboard, overhead projector, or newsprint visible to everyone.

Another lead-in is to have the students write a letter to an hypothetical teenager from another country who is soon to arrive in America. Tell them the letter should be full of advice about how to "make it" in an American high school. Have several students read their letters aloud. Summarize the letters and move to the TalkSheet discussion.

The Discussion:

Item #1: Have the students share the names they chose and the reason they considered these people successful. Then, have them nominate candidates for "the most successful person alive" and conduct a vote to arrive at a "winner". You may wish to amend this to include those who are not still alive, with the exception of Jesus Christ, Moses, etc. This will give you a good idea who the students consider successful.

Item #2: This activity examines the students' priorities concerning success. They must decide which activity is more successful. Have them share their rankings. If there are large discrepancies, allow for a debate. Ask them how they believe God would rank them.

Item #3: Most young people don't think about giving up things. They are focused on accumulating things. This item forces them to consider what is truly important to them and what is not. You may wish to make your own list and have the group decide what they would give up if they had to.

Item #4: Have the students share their choices and state why they were chosen. In each case, have them use scriptural guidelines for their choices. Look for inconsistencies in what they have chosen and point out, in a general way, these inconsistencies. Avoid focusing on a particular person.

Item #5: This activity contrasts secular philosophy with a Biblical one. Point out there is often a sharp contrast between what the Bible says and what the world says.

To Close the Session:

Have each person summarize what they have learned. Challenge them to consider success from God's point of view. Point out how easily we are misled by worldly standards of success rather than by God's.

A good illustration to use is "How to Catch Monkeys": Natives in the African jungle tie a hollowed-out coconut to a tree, with a hole in the coconut just large enough to allow the monkey's fist to pass through. Inside the coconut is a ripe orange or other delectable fruit. When the monkey reaches inside and grips the fruit, he is unable to pull his hand out. The hunter then walks up and captures the avaricious monkey, because the monkey is unwilling to release his grip on the fruit, even to escape. Similarly, people today are often unwilling to let go worldly success in order to inherit the kingdom of God. "What does it profit a man if he should gain the whole world and lose his soul?"

God does want us to have the best in life and to be truly successful, but God knows best how that will be accomplished. If we "seek first the Kingdom of God and His righteousness, all these things will be added unto us."

Outside Activities:

Ask the students to participate in a Christian social service project that helps someone outside the church family.

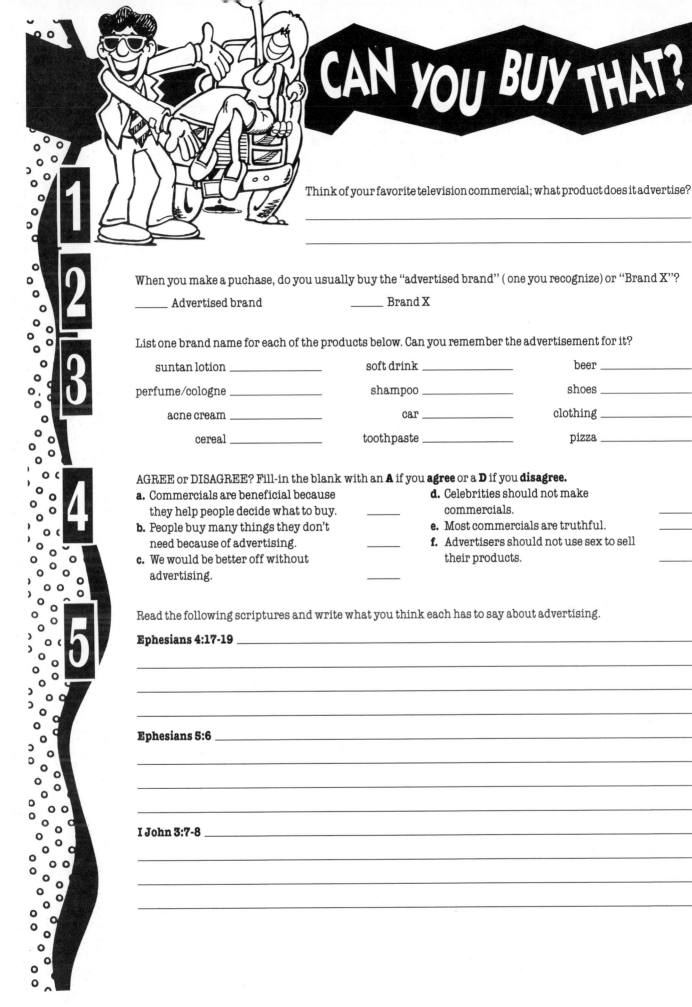

CAN YOU BUY THAT?

1 Think of your favorite television commercial; what product does it advertise?

_____

_____

2 When you make a puchase, do you usually buy the "advertised brand" (one you recognize) or "Brand X"?

_____ Advertised brand   _____ Brand X

3 List one brand name for each of the products below. Can you remember the advertisement for it?

suntan lotion _____   soft drink _____   beer _____

perfume/cologne _____   shampoo _____   shoes _____

acne cream _____   car _____   clothing _____

cereal _____   toothpaste _____   pizza _____

4 AGREE or DISAGREE? Fill-in the blank with an **A** if you **agree** or a **D** if you **disagree.**

a. Commercials are beneficial because they help people decide what to buy. _____

b. People buy many things they don't need because of advertising. _____

c. We would be better off without advertising. _____

d. Celebrities should not make commercials. _____

e. Most commercials are truthful. _____

f. Advertisers should not use sex to sell their products. _____

5 Read the following scriptures and write what you think each has to say about advertising.

Ephesians 4:17-19 _____

_____

_____

_____

Ephesians 5:6 _____

_____

_____

_____

I John 3:7-8 _____

_____

_____

_____

CAN YOU BUY THAT?

Topic: Advertising

Purpose of this Session:

Today's adolescents are bombarded by advertising from every direction. Big business is deliberately attracting whatever monies the young people have. Junior high students are especially vulnerable. They are inexperienced and naive about what they see and hear. You can help them understand how false advertising can manipulate and exploit them with this session.

To Introduce the Topic:

Videotape several commercials and show them to the students. Try to choose those that are humorous and interesting, but also manipulative and deceptive.

Another good lead-in is to make a list of advertising slogans and have the students guess the product each represents. This could be a game, with competing teams and points given for each correct answer.

The Discussion:

Item #1: Let the students share their favorite commercials. You may wish to divide them into groups and act out specific ones, with the rest of the group trying to guess the product.

Item #2: Most will respond by saying "It depends. . ." A good way to handle this is to make two lists, one of *advertised brands* and another, *Brand X*. Then write the reasons given for each "It depends" answer.

Item #3: This should be fun. See how many different brand names can be thought of for each product. Discuss how the students became aware of the brand. Point out how easy it was for them to remember the ads and how the advertisers have influenced their thinking.

Item #4: This was devised to create a variety of responses. Let the students debate the different issues. You might wish to have them "take a stand" for their particular positions, with those that "Agree" on one side of the room and those that "Disagree" on the other. Cover as many points of view as possible and keep the discussion open-minded.

Item #5: Ask for the students' opinions and how they can apply the lessons learned from the scriptures to their daily lives.

To Close the Session:

Stress the fact that no one should be passive about advertising. Everyone should be discerning and observe advertising hype with a critical eye. The advertiser is primarily trying to get people to buy the product and in most cases, cares only about making a profit. Advertising always puts the products in the best possible light. It would be wise to remember that.

Christians need to evaluate advertising according to the values of the kingdom of God and not let themselves be misled. For instance, many advertisements will insist their product will make you happy, or will make others envious of you. We know from the Bible no product can bring happiness; that comes only from God. We also know it is wrong for a follower of Christ to want to make him or herself the envy of others.

On the other hand, inform the students not all advertising is false. There are benefits when the consumer learns everything available about a product. However, a lot of ads are misleading and deceptive. Young people need to realize some of the promises made cannot be kept. For example, the skin creams they use, the clothes they wear, and the soft drinks they consume will not make them beautiful or popular or sexy. Challenge them to use caution ("Buyer Beware") and to be aware of the power of influential ads every day.

Outside Activities:

1. Have the students gather samples of advertising they consider deceptive or misleading and discuss them with the group.

2. Have the students videotape TV commercials they feel are especially designed to attract young people. Show them to the group and discuss their pros and cons.

I WONDER

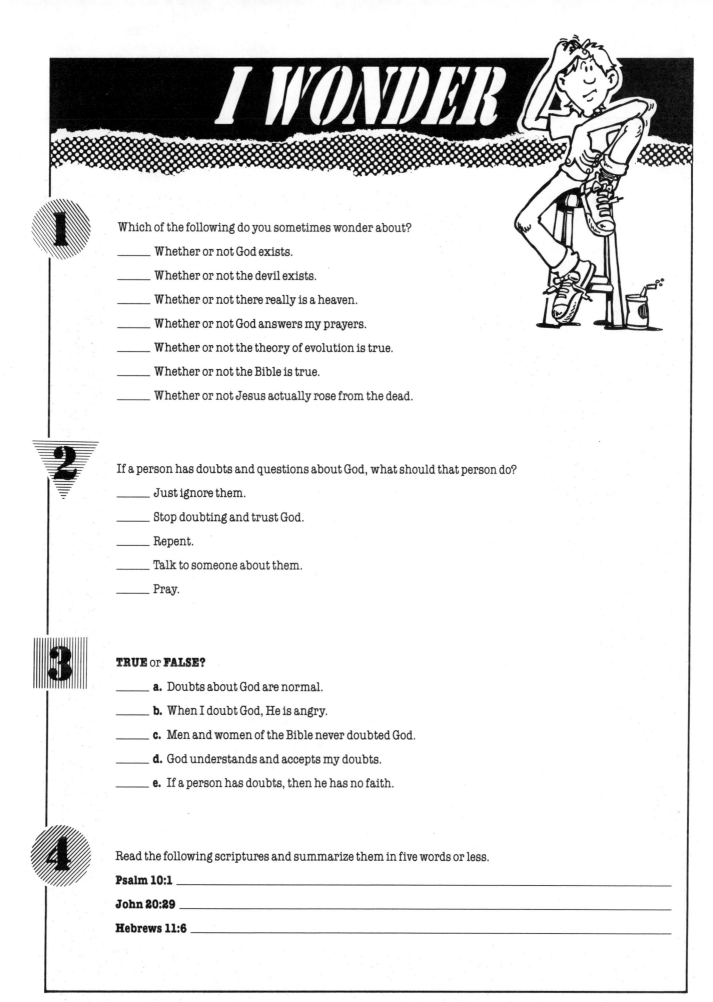

1 Which of the following do you sometimes wonder about?

_____ Whether or not God exists.

_____ Whether or not the devil exists.

_____ Whether or not there really is a heaven.

_____ Whether or not God answers my prayers.

_____ Whether or not the theory of evolution is true.

_____ Whether or not the Bible is true.

_____ Whether or not Jesus actually rose from the dead.

2 If a person has doubts and questions about God, what should that person do?

_____ Just ignore them.

_____ Stop doubting and trust God.

_____ Repent.

_____ Talk to someone about them.

_____ Pray.

3 **TRUE** or **FALSE?**

_____ **a.** Doubts about God are normal.

_____ **b.** When I doubt God, He is angry.

_____ **c.** Men and women of the Bible never doubted God.

_____ **d.** God understands and accepts my doubts.

_____ **e.** If a person has doubts, then he has no faith.

4 Read the following scriptures and summarize them in five words or less.

Psalm 10:1 _____

John 20:29 _____

Hebrews 11:6 _____

I WONDER

Topic: Doubt

Purpose of this Session:

Junior high students are at an age where they have a lot of doubts about the things they have been taught. Doubt, questioning, and even disbelief are normal, healthy adolescent experiences. It is important, therefore, for them to be able to discuss their confusion or potential confusion with responsible adults like yourself. This session is not intended to answer all their questions nor to eliminate any doubts, but to let them know doubting is normal and nothing to feel guilty about.

To Introduce the Topic:

An effective method is to fabricate a personal testimony. Give your group a bogus testimonial concerning how you have lost your faith and are considering abandoning Christianity. Let someone in on your plan, so they can ask you some soul-searching questions, then walk out of the room bristling with disbelief.

Another lead-in is for you to share some of the doubts you had when you were younger and some you just know about. If you choose this method, do not overwhelm the students with bewildering questions. Tension is okay, but too much can lead to confusion.

The Discussion:

Item #1: Some students may be embarrassed to admit they have doubt in any of these areas. Go down the list and ask if any have wondered about each one. If they express no doubts, pressure them a little. For example, say "Since you are so sure about this one, maybe you can help me. Tell me what makes you so certain." If they are being honest, they will admit to having serious doubts about most of these issues. Let them express doubt without passing judgment on them.

Item #2: The purpose of this item is to encourage the students to talk about their doubts and questions. Let them know you are always available to listen to the questions they might have.

Item #3: Use these statements as a vehicle to discuss the fact that doubt is normal for all of us. Reinforce the knowledge that God will not reject us, even for doubting. When the students begin to share some of their doubts, do not feel pressured to supply all the answers. It is all right to say, "I don't know."

Point out doubt is almost *required* in order to strengthen faith. If you are absolutely certain about something, such as the law of gravity, then there is no need for faith. Faith is believing even when you doubt.

Item #4: Let the group share their summaries. Ask them if they think God understands their doubts.

To Close the Session:

Tell the story of John the Baptist — how he confidently announced the coming of Christ and then, when he was thrown into prison, began to have doubts about whether or not Jesus was who He said He was (Luke 7:18-23).

Reiterate the fact that doubts are normal. Having doubt does not mean being without faith. Doubting is not sinning. Challenge your students to stretch their minds and keep searching for a deeper, more meaningful truth. Encourage them to talk to people they trust, people who really care about them as individuals.

Outside Activities:

1. Have the students research the scriptures for examples of people who expressed doubt. Have them share their findings.

2. Ask the students to interview members of the congregation concerning any doubts they have had about their Christianity and then have them share their interviews.

OH, GOD

1   Circle the words below you think best describe what God is like.

holy	loving	policeman	smart	American	freak
powerful	dead	mysterious	motherly	fatherly	out-of-it

2   If you could ask God one question, what would it be? _____

_____

_____

_____

_____

_____

3   If God wrote you a personal letter, what do you think He would say to you?

Dear _____,

_____

_____

_____

_____

_____

_____

                                    Sincerely,

                                         God.

4   Brian has always believed in God, but he has never felt really close to God nor felt that God actually cared about him. See if you can give Brian some suggestions about how he can get to know God better.

_____

_____

_____

_____

_____

_____

5   Look up the following scriptures and decide which ones describe God and which ones do not.

Romans 11:33	Romans 12:1	Psalm 118:29	John 4:24
Matthew 7:11		Matthew 6:33	Deuteronomy 32:4

Date Used: _____

Group: _____

OH, GOD

Topic: God

Purpose of this Session:

It is always a good idea to give young people the opportunity to think about their reasons for believing in God, what God is like and how their belief in God makes a difference in their lives. This TalkSheet was designed to create just such a discussion.

To Introduce the Topic:

The following are good ideas to encourage your students to think about God:

1. Have them search for evidence of God in newspapers and magazines. The results will be amazing. Allow each to share his or her findings.

2. Divide the students into small groups and have each complete the sentence. "God is like. . .". They should use comparatives with reference to the modern world, such as "God is like Coke — He's the Real Thing!"

3. Have small groups of students each create a skit as a "commercial for God". Allow time for the skits to be presented.

The Discussion:

Item #1: Have the students share the words they chose and think of additional words to describe God.

Item #2: Let the students share their questions and try to answer them as a group. Some simply will not have anwers, so don't get bogged down. Help them understand God has answers to our questions, even though sometimes we don't know what they are.

Item #3: Ask several students to share their letters and what they learned from this exercise. Emphasize God has *already* written us a letter: the Bible. The Bible is God's love letter to each of us and we need to read it, often.

Item #4: Use this "Tension Getter" to discuss practical ways to have a better relationship with God. Make a master list of all the suggestions the students think of. You may want to add some of your own. Ask the students to choose one to put into practice this week.

Item #5: Have the students report their findings on these verses. Ask them to relate what they learned about God from the ones that describe Him.

To Close the Session:

Close with a time of prayer — talking to God. If your junior high students are too self-conscious to pray aloud, try asking them to write a one-sentence prayer on the back of their TalkSheet. Then, ask someone else to read them. You might also allow time for silent prayer.

Another good close is to present a message about "What God Thinks of You." Emphasize God loves them as they are and not as they think they should be. ("If God had a wallet, your picture would be in it!")

Remind your students it is not enough just to "believe" in God. We need to act like we believe in Him. Ask them how their lifestyles can exemplify their belief in God.

Other Activities:

Have the group select several Psalms to study. After reading them, have them write out five things they learned about God. They can then share their findings.

TRUST ME

1 Circle all those in the following list you think you could trust:

The President	**your mom**	**a door-to-door salesman**	**God**
your brother or sister	**a school teacher**	**a TV star**	**your father**
a police officer	**yourself**	**a stranger**	**a rock star**

2 Circle the most honest answer:

My parents can trust me . . .

a. all of the time

b. some of the time

c. never

My teachers can trust me . . .

a. all of the time

b. some of the time

c. they can't

My friends can trust me . . .

a. with anything

b. with everything but a secret

c. they can't

3 Remember an occassion when you were trustworthy, and describe the situation. _____

_____

_____

_____

_____

_____

4 AGREE or DISAGREE?

	AGREE	DISAGREE
a. The average person can usually be trusted.	☐	☐
b. It is better to trust Christians than non-Christians.	☐	☐
c. It is difficult to know who to trust these days.	☐	☐
d. Once a person lies to you or doesn't keep their promise, it is impossible to trust them again.	☐	☐
e. It is best not to trust anyone.	☐	☐

5 Rewrite **Proverbs 3:5-6** in your own words.

_____

_____

_____

_____

_____

_____

Date Used: _____

Group: _____

TRUST ME

Topic: Trust

Purpose of this Session:

Early adolescence often brings the first experience of betrayal. Young people learn there are some people who cannot be trusted. But what of the Christian and trust? How much trust should Christians extend to others and how trustworthy should Christians be?

To Introduce the Topic:

Divide the students into pairs with one member of each couple keeping their eyes closed for a "blind walk". The seeing partner then leads the "blind" one around the church property. The seeing person is responsible for the safety of the "blind" one. Have them reverse roles and repeat the experiment. Discuss the feelings each experienced. Was it difficult to trust? How did the seeing person help or hinder the trust in the relationship? Discuss both the good and bad experiences.

The Discussion:

Item #1: Ask the students to share the words they circled. Ask why they think they can trust the persons chosen. Have them pick out three people they consider the most trustworthy of all.

Item #2: This brings the trust issue closer to home. Some may not want to reveal their answers, so don't force them. Instead, ask them how many would like to be trustworthy all the time and if they have any ideas about how to become that kind of person. Talk about trust being the basis of a good relationship. The less trust there is, the less of a relationship there is.

Item #3: Ask the students to share any experiences here, if any. You can expand this question by asking if they can think of a time when a friend demonstrated they could be trusted or if they remember a time when a friend betrayed a trust. They should not disclose any names, however.

Item #4: Take a poll on each of these issues and discuss each one. Ask the students to explain why they feel as they do. Be positive as you help them confront these statements. Help them see trust is necessary and important for good relationships and self-respect. If someone blows it, they need to be forgiven and trust re-established.

Item #5: Have the students share their sentences. Discuss how a person can trust God no matter what. Try to put this into practical terms. How can we trust God in our daily lives? Help them see that God and His word (the Bible) can be trusted even when we ourselves cannot.

To Close the Session:

Challenge the students to be trustworthy. They will not always be able to trust some people but they can be trustworthy themselves. Trust must be earned and it must be developed over time. No one automatically deserves to be trusted. Trust is a treasure to be cherished, an asset. Once it is violated, it is difficult to restore to its original state. Young people should not be surprised if their parents or friends don't trust them after they have been untrustworthy. There is an old saying that states, "There's only one thing finer than having a friend you can trust — and that's being trustworthy yourself."

Outside Activities:

Have your students make an effort to do one thing at home to build trust with their family. Ask them to write down what they did and what the results were.

THIS MEANS WAR!

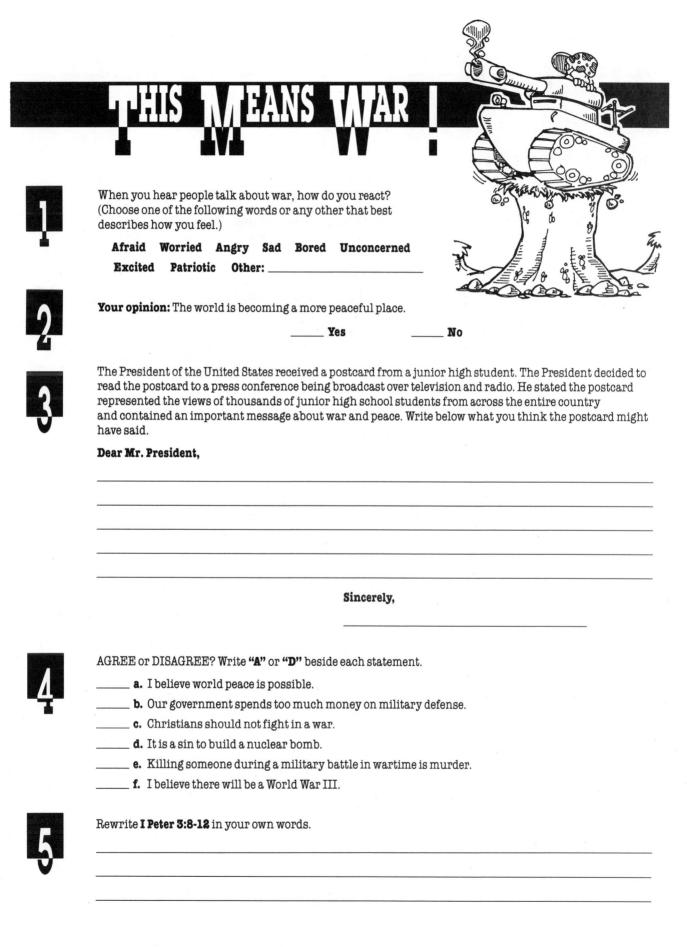

1 When you hear people talk about war, how do you react? (Choose one of the following words or any other that best describes how you feel.)

Afraid   Worried   Angry   Sad   Bored   Unconcerned
Excited   Patriotic   Other: _____

2 **Your opinion:** The world is becoming a more peaceful place.

_____ **Yes**   _____ **No**

3 The President of the United States received a postcard from a junior high student. The President decided to read the postcard to a press conference being broadcast over television and radio. He stated the postcard represented the views of thousands of junior high school students from across the entire country and contained an important message about war and peace. Write below what you think the postcard might have said.

Dear Mr. President,

_____

_____

_____

_____

_____

Sincerely,

_____

4 AGREE or DISAGREE? Write **"A"** or **"D"** beside each statement.

_____ **a.** I believe world peace is possible.

_____ **b.** Our government spends too much money on military defense.

_____ **c.** Christians should not fight in a war.

_____ **d.** It is a sin to build a nuclear bomb.

_____ **e.** Killing someone during a military battle in wartime is murder.

_____ **f.** I believe there will be a World War III.

5 Rewrite **I Peter 3:8-12** in your own words.

_____

_____

_____

Date Used: _____

Group: _____

THIS MEANS WAR!

Topic: War

Purpose of this Session:

Unfortunately we live in a world that is not free from war. Wars are in progress all over the globe and are brought into our homes via television. The threat of nuclear war is a real, persistent threat. Junior high students hear about war, think about war, worry about war and often see it glamourized in movies ("Rambo") or in "G.I. Joe" comics. This TalkSheet will allow you to help your students think about the subject from a Christian perspective.

If you or your church takes a strong position on either side of the war and peace issue, you may use this discussion as a way to help your students understand your view as well as to formulate one of their own.

To Introduce the Topic:

Divide the students into small groups. Each should pretend they are commanders of a U.S. nuclear site hidden and protected in an underground site. The group has the task of launching a nuclear warhead upon a city inside the Soviet Union. They are the only missile site aimed at this city. The command comes from the President to launch the missile. The Soviets have already launched their missile. Americans will most certainly be killed whether or not the president's launch order is obeyed. Each group has five minutes to decide whether or not to launch their reciprocal missile. Find out what each group decided to do. Debrief the experience by telling the group you are going to discuss war using the TalkSheet.

The Discussion:

Item #1: If responses are slow on this, ask how they would feel in resonse to specific headlines, such as: "IRAN AND U.S. MOVING CLOSER TO WAR", or "RUSSIA WARNS U.S. TO STOP TESTING 'STAR WARS' DEFENSE SYSTEM". Allow enough time for the students to share their fears about the possibility of a nuclear war.

Item #2: Poll the students to see how they voted and why.

Item #3: Have several students read their letters. Then see if they can come up with some concrete, specific ideas about how to prevent war, such as writing the Soviet Premier and the President of the U.S.

Item #4: You may wish to let the "Agrees" and the "Disgrees" have a debate. Provide input for them on items they are confused about. Keep in mind some of these issues are not directly addressed in scripture, so there are many points of view, even among Christians.

Item #5: Ask how this scripture relates to World War. Does it also relate to family fights? Disagreements with friends? Another verse to consider is James 4:1-2.

To Close the Session:

Challenge your students to be peacemakers as Christ commanded. They could begin in the youth group, their schools, and their families.

Help them understand war is a terrible thing and should not be taken lightly. As Christians, we must reject violence and death as a way of solving problems in the world. Christian young people must say "no" to war, and do everything they can to promote peace and understanding.

Give your students some hope. Don't send them home depressed. Let them know God is still in control of the world, even though the situation looks impossible at times. We don't have to be afraid. We can face the future with hope and confidence because God is with us.

Outside Activities:

1. Assign one of the tasks they considered in discussing Item #3.

2. Have the group created anti-war posters, with slogans such as "It's a sin to build a nuclear bomb."

BIG MOUTH

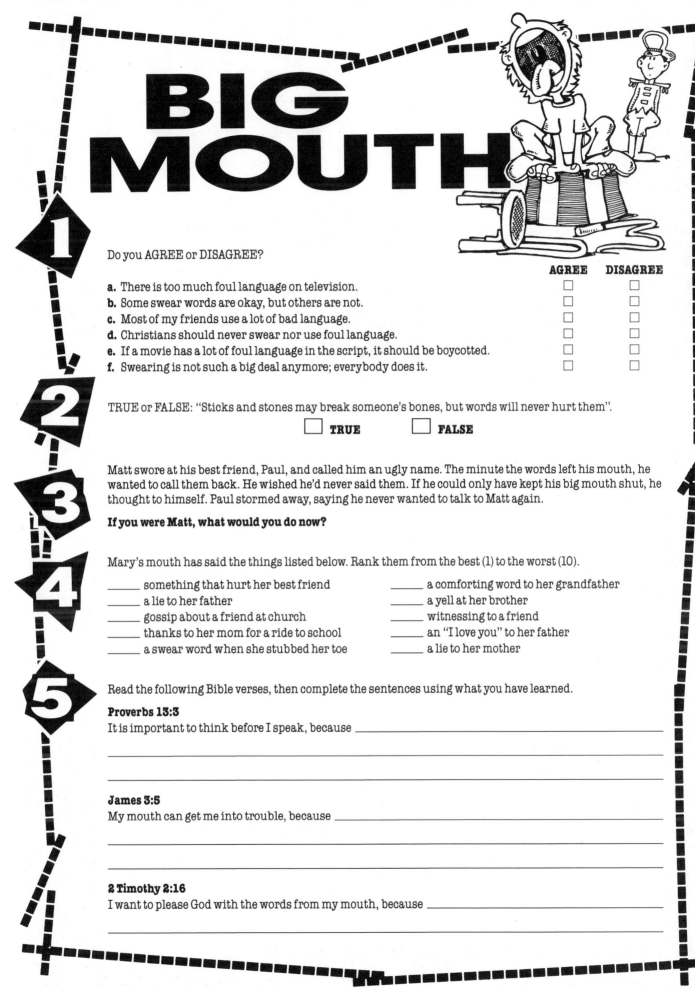

1 Do you AGREE or DISAGREE?

	AGREE	DISAGREE
a. There is too much foul language on television.	☐	☐
b. Some swear words are okay, but others are not.	☐	☐
c. Most of my friends use a lot of bad language.	☐	☐
d. Christians should never swear nor use foul language.	☐	☐
e. If a movie has a lot of foul language in the script, it should be boycotted.	☐	☐
f. Swearing is not such a big deal anymore; everybody does it.	☐	☐

2 TRUE or FALSE: "Sticks and stones may break someone's bones, but words will never hurt them".

☐ **TRUE**   ☐ **FALSE**

3 Matt swore at his best friend, Paul, and called him an ugly name. The minute the words left his mouth, he wanted to call them back. He wished he'd never said them. If he could only have kept his big mouth shut, he thought to himself. Paul stormed away, saying he never wanted to talk to Matt again.

If you were Matt, what would you do now?

4 Mary's mouth has said the things listed below. Rank them from the best (1) to the worst (10).

_____ something that hurt her best friend   _____ a comforting word to her grandfather
_____ a lie to her father   _____ a yell at her brother
_____ gossip about a friend at church   _____ witnessing to a friend
_____ thanks to her mom for a ride to school   _____ an "I love you" to her father
_____ a swear word when she stubbed her toe   _____ a lie to her mother

5 Read the following Bible verses, then complete the sentences using what you have learned.

Proverbs 13:3
It is important to think before I speak, because _____
_____
_____

James 3:5
My mouth can get me into trouble, because _____
_____
_____

2 Timothy 2:16
I want to please God with the words from my mouth, because _____
_____

BIG MOUTH

Topic: Taming the tongue

Purpose of this Sesssion:

Since the time of Adam and Eve, the human race has had difficulty controlling its tongue. But it has only been recently that young people have been exposed so frequently to rough language and inappropriate speech. Teen movies starring young celebrities using foul language, gossiping and hurting others by what they say are being depicted as normal and accepted behavior. This TalkSheet will help you discuss the relationship between the Christian faith and the words we use.

To Introduce the Session:

Conduct a "compliment contest". Ask one person to be "it" and a few others to participate in the contest to see who can give the nicest compliment to the person who is "it". Offer a prize to the winner. The person being complimented can choose the best compliment or you can have a panel of judges to decide.

After the game, ask why it is so difficult sometimes to say nice things to each other on a day-to-day basis. It seems most of the time we have to endure put-downs, gossip, slams, digs, foul language and rude comments from each other. Let's talk about talk and how what we say to each other makes a big difference.

Another good lead-in is to play "The Gossip Game". The first student in a circle whispers a Bible verse in the ear of the person to his or her right, and then the second person repeats the whisper to the person next in line, and so on. The object is to see if the last person in line gets the verse in its original form. Usually the verse becomes distorted, which is a good illustration of how rumors and gossip work in real life.

The Discussion:

Item #1: This deals with the issue of swearing. In all probability, swearing (cussing, foul language) is common with junior high students. Discuss each of these statements and help them understand it is important for Christians to speak in ways that glorify God. When we swear and use obscenities, we do not glorify God, we are being poor witnesses for Him and we are showing disrespect for those around us. Emphasize swearing is not "cool" or funny, even though the media would have us believe otherwise. Usually, bad language is used when the scriptwriters are not creative enough to think of anything else to write.

Item #2: Show the old saying "Sticks and stones. . ." is a myth. Words really do hurt and can cause irreversible damage.

Item #3: Use this "Tension Getter" to discuss practical ways to control one's tongue. Ask if anyone in the group has ever experienced anything similar. You might have two of the students role-play the characters Matt and Paul. Have them decide what the long-term results of Matt's actions might be.

Item #4: Have the students share their ranking choices and give their reasons. See if you can decide as a group which is the worst.

Item #5: Ask the students to read their sentences. Discuss each of the scriptures in practical terms.

To Close the Session:

Summarize the major points made. Help the students understand words are not neutral. The philosopher Pascal once said "Cold words freeze people and hot words scorch them; bitter words make them bitter and wrathful words make them wrathful." Conversely, kind and thoughtful words do wonders. Christians should be generous with them.

Many times we say things we shouldn't and then wish the words were attached to a rope, so we could pull them back out of the air. We can't. Encourage your students to think before they curse a teacher, say something hurtful to a parent, or gossip about a friend.

Outside Activities:

Assign several TV shows to be watched by your students. Tell them to count the number of times foul language is used. The same can be done for movies. Talk about the results of the survey with the group.

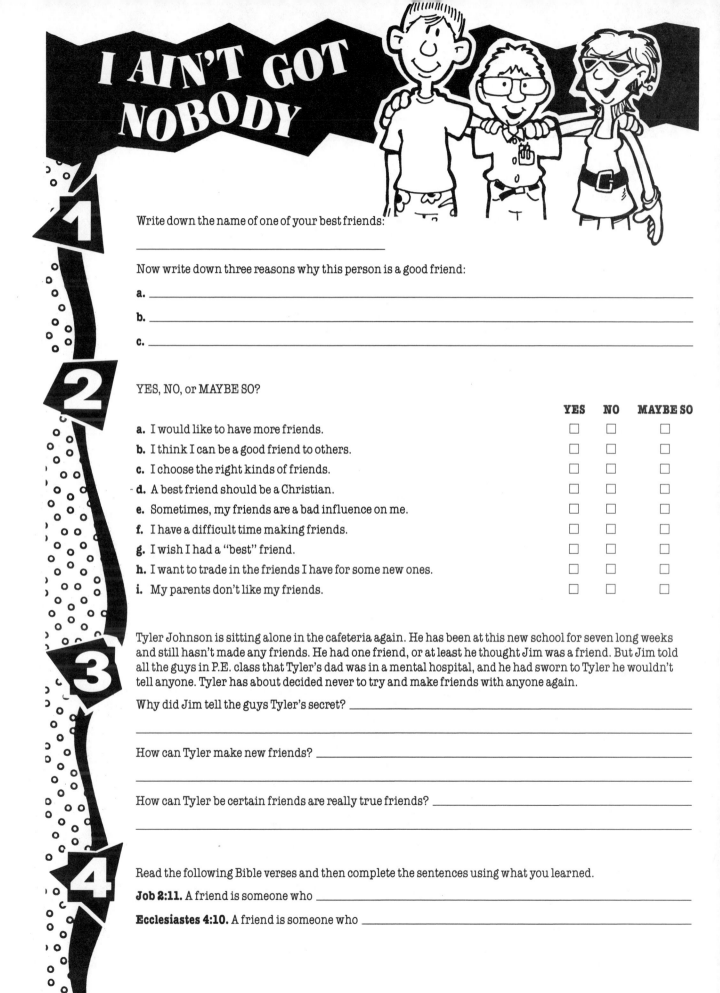

I AIN'T GOT NOBODY

1 Write down the name of one of your best friends:

_____

Now write down three reasons why this person is a good friend:

a. _____

b. _____

c. _____

2 YES, NO, or MAYBE SO?

	YES	NO	MAYBE SO
a. I would like to have more friends.	☐	☐	☐
b. I think I can be a good friend to others.	☐	☐	☐
c. I choose the right kinds of friends.	☐	☐	☐
d. A best friend should be a Christian.	☐	☐	☐
e. Sometimes, my friends are a bad influence on me.	☐	☐	☐
f. I have a difficult time making friends.	☐	☐	☐
g. I wish I had a "best" friend.	☐	☐	☐
h. I want to trade in the friends I have for some new ones.	☐	☐	☐
i. My parents don't like my friends.	☐	☐	☐

3 Tyler Johnson is sitting alone in the cafeteria again. He has been at this new school for seven long weeks and still hasn't made any friends. He had one friend, or at least he thought Jim was a friend. But Jim told all the guys in P.E. class that Tyler's dad was in a mental hospital, and he had sworn to Tyler he wouldn't tell anyone. Tyler has about decided never to try and make friends with anyone again.

Why did Jim tell the guys Tyler's secret? _____

_____

How can Tyler make new friends? _____

_____

How can Tyler be certain friends are really true friends? _____

_____

4 Read the following Bible verses and then complete the sentences using what you learned.

Job 2:11. A friend is someone who _____

Ecclesiastes 4:10. A friend is someone who _____

I AIN'T GOT NOBODY

Topic: Friendship

Purpose of this Session:

Having friends is the primary concern of adolescents. There is hardly anything as important to junior high students than their circle of friends. They will always be interested in learning about friends — how to get them, how to keep them, how to get rid of them, and how to be one. This TalkSheet will help your group discuss friendship from a Christian perspective.

To Introduce the Topic:

If your group is large enough, play the "famous friends" game. Give everyone a slip of paper with one half of a famous couple written on it, such as Cagney and Lacey, Mickey Mouse and Donald Duck, Laurel and Hardy, etc. Then tell them to find their partners without speaking aloud and without showing anyone their slips of paper. They have to pantomime the characters in order to identify each other.

Another good lead-in is to make a long list of "qualities of a good friend" on the blackboard, which can include such things as having a lot of money, popularity, intelligence, strong Christianity, kindness, considerate, good looks, sense of humor, access to a car, honesty, sex appeal, same age, has no other friends, lives nearby, good personality, etc. Then tell the students they can choose five qualities for a friend of their own. (Or any number you decide.) Which would be the most important to them? Have a few students share their choices.

The Discussion:

Item #1: Have the students talk about their friends and why they are good friends.

Item #2: Discuss each item on the list and ask for volunteers to share their answers. Some answers will be more threatening than others. The best way to discuss these is to create new questions about each, such as (a) How can a person make new friends? and (i) Why do you think parents might not like your friends?

A good general question here is "What did you learn from these statements?" Some will say they realize they would like to have more friends. Encourage them to befriend someone not already in their immediate circle. Talk about the obstacles sometimes encountered when trying to make friends outside their clique.

Item #3: Use this "Tension Getter" to discuss betrayal by friends. This is a concept many of your students have only recently learned. It is difficult for them to understand why friends would betray or hurt them. Let them share how they feel.

Item #4: Have the students share their completed sentences.

To Close the Session:

Read Proverbs 18:24: "A good friend shows himself friendly." In other words, if we want to have good friends, then we need to be a good friend. Friendships rarely happen by accident. They need mutual nourishment, consideration and effort.

Let your junior high students know God wants them to have good friends. Jesus Himself had many good friends, a close group of men and women with whom He spent a lot of time. He frequently taught how to be a good friend and neighbor to others and how to relate to people in a positive way.

Jesus also wants to be our friend. He is a friend who "sticks closer than a brother". If we have Christ as our friend, we will have many other friends who also know about Christ. That is what the youth group is all about. We are the friends of Jesus.

Close with a prayer asking Christ to draw everyone in the youth group closer together in friendship, united in Him.

Outside Activities:

1. Have the students pretend they are applying for a job as a friend. As part of the application, they are to list all the qualifications they have for being a friend.

2. Create a Big Brother/Big Sister program for one Sunday. Assign each of your group members to a fifth or sixth grade student for the day. They can sit together during church, talk about the junior high group, etc.

KIDS JUST WANT TO HAVE FUN

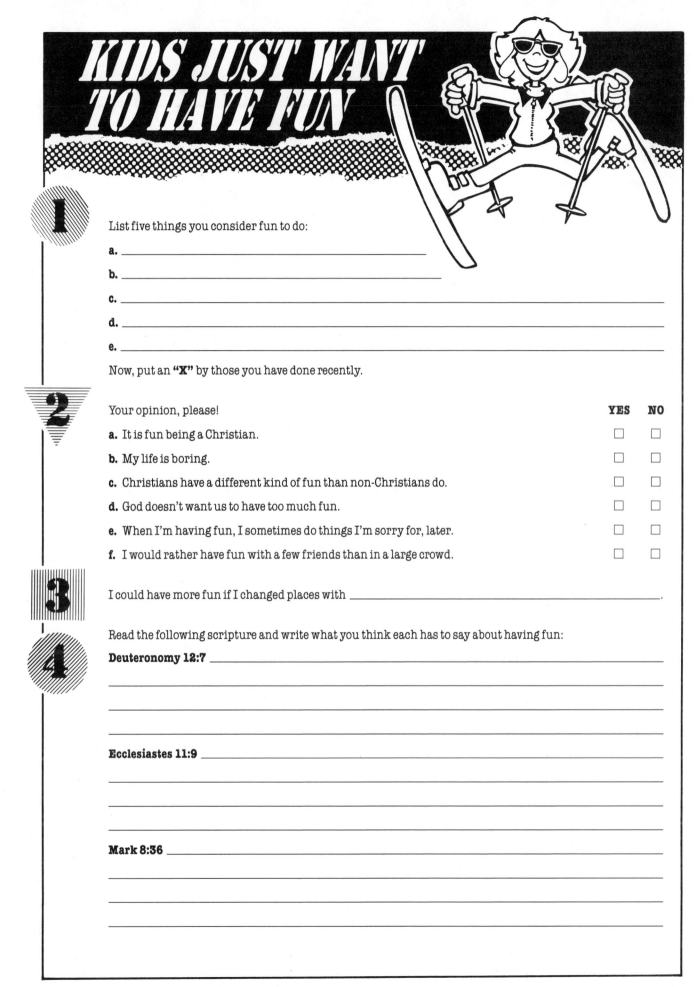

1

List five things you consider fun to do:

a. _____

b. _____

c. _____

d. _____

e. _____

Now, put an **"X"** by those you have done recently.

2

Your opinion, please!

	YES	NO
a. It is fun being a Christian.	☐	☐
b. My life is boring.	☐	☐
c. Christians have a different kind of fun than non-Christians do.	☐	☐
d. God doesn't want us to have too much fun.	☐	☐
e. When I'm having fun, I sometimes do things I'm sorry for, later.	☐	☐
f. I would rather have fun with a few friends than in a large crowd.	☐	☐

3

I could have more fun if I changed places with _____.

4

Read the following scripture and write what you think each has to say about having fun:

Deuteronomy 12:7 _____

_____

_____

_____

Ecclesiastes 11:9 _____

_____

_____

_____

Mark 8:36 _____

_____

_____

_____

_____

Date Used: _____

Group: _____

KIDS JUST WANT TO HAVE FUN

Topic: Fun

Purpose of this Session:

Many young people don't know how to have fun. They are growing up so fast they have forgotten how to play. If someone acts zany, crazy or uninhibited in a healthy way, they think he or she is stoned or drunk. They need to learn how to have fun creatively and safely. This TalkSheet will help you talk about having fun.

To Introduce the Topic:

Have some fun! Involve the parents in this by having them bring a variety of fun food. Let the students bring their favorite Christian albums and videos. Have several lead the group in their favorite games.

The Discussion:

Item #1: Make a master list of the things your group considers "fun". The list can include both positive and negative items. Keep the list visible on a chalkboard or newsprint to refer to, later.

Ask the students to share which ones they placed an "X" beside, indicating they have done those recently. In what ways were those activities fun? Which activities have they never done? Why not?

Item #2: Take these statements one at a time and ask for a show of hands on each one. Ask the reasons for each one. Find out why, or why not, Christians have fun or why they think their life is boring, or why they think God is against fun. Focus on the need for many young people to have constant excitement in their lives. Young people who are always living on the edge are headed for trouble. Partying has beome a major sport for many. Wholesome fun is healthy. Misguided fun can be dangerous.

Item #3: Ask why they chose the person named on this item. What is it about the person that makes them think they would have more fun if they were that person? Could they ever become like that person?

Item #4: You might wish to divide the students into smaller groups to decide what each of these scriptures has to say about fun.

To Close the Session:

The following are key points to emphasize:

(1) God does want us to have fun. God is not a "cosmic killjoy" — a corrective parent — sitting up in heaven with a frown on his face. He wants us to enjoy life at its fullest. He is the creator of life and therefore, He knows what is best for us and how we can get the most out of life. Read Phillippians 4:4. Paul encourages us to "rejoice".

(2) Help the students realize it is possible to "party" without getting into trouble. They will probably encounter many situations, especially as they grow older, when they will be confronted with making decisions about drugs and alcohol. Too many young people believe "fun" is synonymous with "getting wasted". Losing control of one's faculties is not fun. Risking irreversible brain damage is not "fun". Encourage your students to pursue wholesome fun activities without doing anything they will regret, later.

Outside Activities:

Plan a fun activity with your junior high students that is really wild and different. Brainstorm ideas with them and your youth leaders, or check out some of the great ideas in the *Ideas* books, published by Youth Specialties, or *Creative Socials and Special Events* by Wayne Rice and Mike Yaconelli (Zondervan/Youth Specialties, 1986)

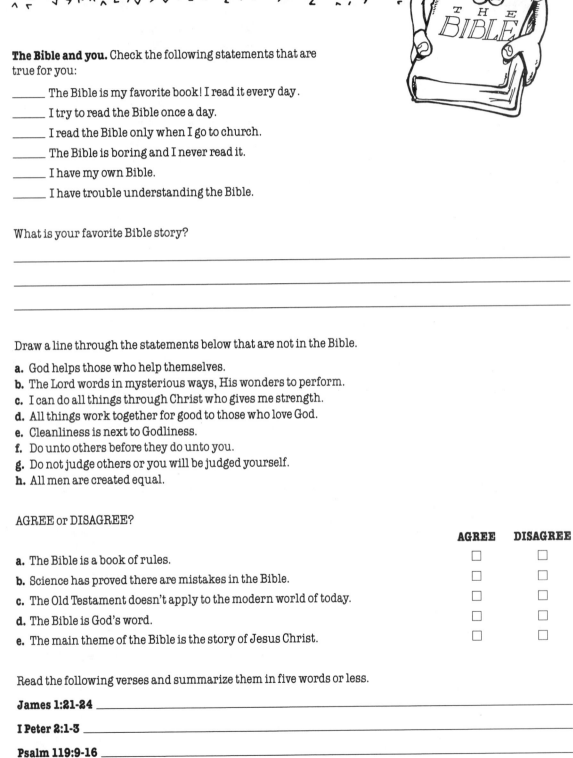

THE BOOK

1 **The Bible and you.** Check the following statements that are true for you:

_____ The Bible is my favorite book! I read it every day.

_____ I try to read the Bible once a day.

_____ I read the Bible only when I go to church.

_____ The Bible is boring and I never read it.

_____ I have my own Bible.

_____ I have trouble understanding the Bible.

2 What is your favorite Bible story?

_____

_____

_____

3 Draw a line through the statements below that are not in the Bible.

a. God helps those who help themselves.

b. The Lord words in mysterious ways, His wonders to perform.

c. I can do all things through Christ who gives me strength.

d. All things work together for good to those who love God.

e. Cleanliness is next to Godliness.

f. Do unto others before they do unto you.

g. Do not judge others or you will be judged yourself.

h. All men are created equal.

4 AGREE or DISAGREE?

	AGREE	DISAGREE
a. The Bible is a book of rules.	☐	☐
b. Science has proved there are mistakes in the Bible.	☐	☐
c. The Old Testament doesn't apply to the modern world of today.	☐	☐
d. The Bible is God's word.	☐	☐
e. The main theme of the Bible is the story of Jesus Christ.	☐	☐

5 Read the following verses and summarize them in five words or less.

James 1:21-24 _____

I Peter 2:1-3 _____

Psalm 119:9-16 _____

THE BOOK

Topic: The Bible

Purpose of this Session:

The young people of today regard the Bible differently from past generations. They do not necessarily believe the Bible is God's Word or that it has authority over their lives. This session provides the opportunity to discuss the Bible, what today's young people think of it, and how Christians should regard the Bible.

To Introduce the Topic:

Have the following quiz: Write the names given below on poster board or chalkboard, visible to all. They must decide which are books in the Bible and which are not, without looking at the Bible's table of contents.

Hezekiah	Timothy	Judas
Philippians	Matthew	Deuteronomy
Romans	Uzziah	Obadiah
Acts	Nahum	Silas
Laminations	Numbers	Bartholomew

Another good lead-in is to conduct a short Bible quiz, using questions from a Bible quiz book.

The Discussion:

Item #1: Let the students share their feelings about the Bible. Give them the opportunity to be open and honest, without judging them.

Item #2: Have the students share their favorite stories. Ask why they became favorites.

Item #3: Statements a, b, e, f and h are not in the Bible. Statement c is Philippians 4:13, d is Romans 8:28 and g is Matthew 7:1.

Item #4: Call for a vote on the statements. If there is disagreement, discuss the issue with the group. Ask the students to explain why they agree or disagree. You will need to be prepared to give your own views, or the views of your church in response to some of the questions raised. Allow enough time for any questions they might have.

Item #5: Encourage the students to develop a consistent habit of studying the Bible. Point out the importance of God's Word for guidance in their daily lives.

To Close the Session:

Help the junior high students understand the Bible is God's Word to us; He reveals Himself to us through the Bible. It is His love letter to us and a source of strength and encouragement.

Encourage your students to obtain a translation of the Bible they can understand readily and to read it daily. Suggest they memorize a few key scriptures they can remember when they need to think about God's perspective.

You might close by having the students share their favorite Bible verses with each other or have your adult leaders share theirs.

Outside Activities:

1. Using one of their favorite Bible stories as a theme, have the group create a poster or a banner.

2. Create a Bible trivia game with the students by writing questions based on the Bible. The game can be played at your next meeting or retreat.

THE CHOICE IS YOURS

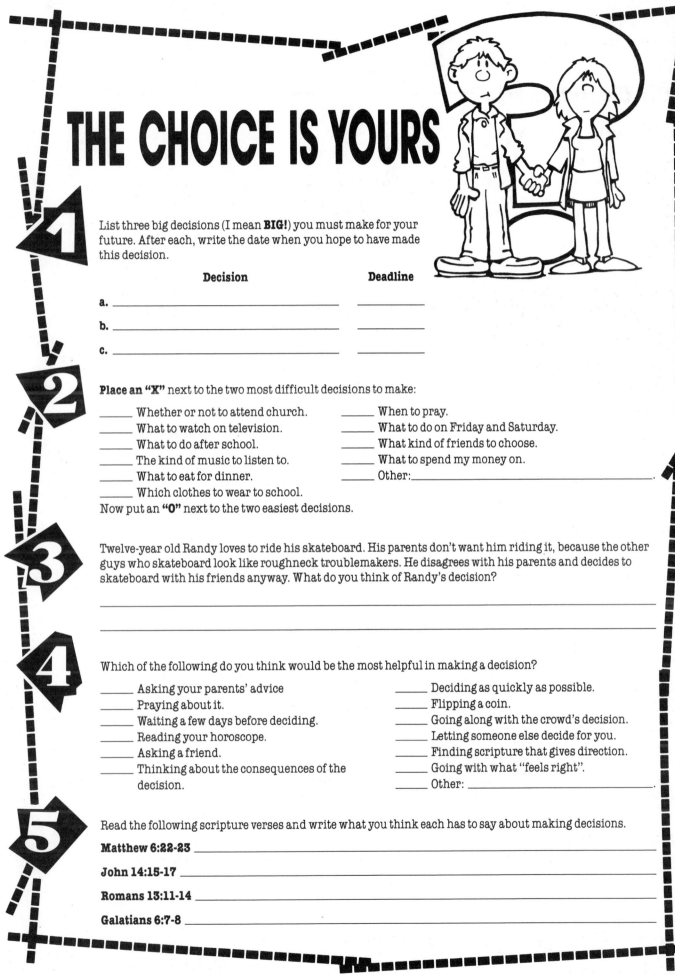

1 List three big decisions (I mean **BIG!**) you must make for your future. After each, write the date when you hope to have made this decision.

	Decision	Deadline
a.	_____	_____
b.	_____	_____
c.	_____	_____

2 **Place an "X"** next to the two most difficult decisions to make:

_____ Whether or not to attend church.　　　　_____ When to pray.

_____ What to watch on television.　　　　_____ What to do on Friday and Saturday.

_____ What to do after school.　　　　_____ What kind of friends to choose.

_____ The kind of music to listen to.　　　　_____ What to spend my money on.

_____ What to eat for dinner.　　　　_____ Other:_____.

_____ Which clothes to wear to school.

Now put an **"O"** next to the two easiest decisions.

3 Twelve-year old Randy loves to ride his skateboard. His parents don't want him riding it, because the other guys who skateboard look like roughneck troublemakers. He disagrees with his parents and decides to skateboard with his friends anyway. What do you think of Randy's decision?

_____

_____

4 Which of the following do you think would be the most helpful in making a decision?

_____ Asking your parents' advice　　　　_____ Deciding as quickly as possible.

_____ Praying about it.　　　　_____ Flipping a coin.

_____ Waiting a few days before deciding.　　　　_____ Going along with the crowd's decision.

_____ Reading your horoscope.　　　　_____ Letting someone else decide for you.

_____ Asking a friend.　　　　_____ Finding scripture that gives direction.

_____ Thinking about the consequences of the　　　　_____ Going with what "feels right".

decision.　　　　_____ Other: _____.

5 Read the following scripture verses and write what you think each has to say about making decisions.

Matthew 6:22-23 _____

John 14:15-17 _____

Romans 13:11-14 _____

Galatians 6:7-8 _____

Date Used: _____

Group: _____

THE CHOICE IS YOURS

Topic: Decision-making

Purpose of the Session:

According to research, junior high students are developing a strong desire to begin making their own decisions on matters of importance to them. As a result, they are faced with a wide range of decisions with very little decision-making experience. This TalkSheet explores the subject of decision-making from a Christian perspective.

To Introduce the Topic:

The following simple game will work well as a lead-in. Gift wrap three items differently — one large, one small, another plain and ugly, one decorated elaborately, etc. Announce one contains something they would like, another contains something worthless and the other contains nothing at all. Divide them into three groups to decide which they would like to have. They cannot touch the gifts before deciding. Once they have made up their minds, draw straws to see which group gets to choose first, second and third.

There will probably be a lot of disagreement in each group, but a decision will have to be made. After the gifts have been awarded (the good one can contain candy or some inexpensive prize — the bad ones, trash or an apple core) tell the group, "Since you had such a difficult time deciding which gift you wanted, perhaps this would be a good time to discuss decision-making."

The Discussion:

Item #1: Have the students share the "big decisions" they anticipate making. Find out which ones the group has in common.

Item #2: Ask the students to share the toughest-to-make decisions as well as the easiest-to-make. Ask why some are more difficult than others. Ask them to share any they thought of that weren't listed.

Item #3: Ask for sharing of the advice they have for Randy. Use this "Tension Getter" to discuss the importance of listening to parents' advice. Help them try to understand the parents' point of view. "Why would the parents be concerned? At 12, does Randy have the ability to decide for himself what he can or cannot do? If not, when does he have that right?" Have the group brainstorm ways to get parents to listen to them and to arrive at a compromise.

Item #4: Use this item to talk about the practical "how-to's" of making decisions: (1) gather all the facts, (2) consider the alternatives, (3) get some good advice, (4) pray, (5) think of every consequence possible, and (6) choose the best possible alternative.

Item #5: Have the students relate these scriptures to practical situations in the lives of today's teens. Encourage them to seek God's perspective when making decisions.

To Close the Session:

Point out big decisions the students make are nothing more than a combination of little decisions. The choices they make today are the bricks in the foundation of the rest of their lives. They may not seem big, but if they can get into the habit of making wise decisions about little things, they will be more confident when it is time to make important ones.

Help them realize they will make much better decisions if they seek good advice and think about the consequences of their decisions. "And then what?" They also need to remember God will help them make decisions. If we pray, consult the Bible, and ask advice from others, we will be much more likely to make a wise decision.

Make certain your students know a wrong decision is okay and unavoidable, once in a while. Everybody makes the wrong choice occasionally. The key is to learn from our mistakes, not dwell on our past wrong decisions, and try to develop good judgment.

Outside Activities:

Have the group develop a presentation for your church's junior department entitled "Decisions Christians Must Make in Junior High School."

LOOKING UP

1 My church worship service is . . . (Place an **"X"** on the line below)

• • • • • • •

Never boring   **Sometimes boring**   **Always boring**

2 Complete the sentence, "My church's worship service would be better if _____

_____

_____

_____"

3 What do you think is the most important part of a worship service?

_____ the choir	_____ prayer	_____ scripture reading
_____ the sermon	_____ offering	_____ announcements
_____ singing hymns	_____ communion	_____ special music
		_____ other: _____

4 Your opinion, please!

	YES	NO
a. The best place to worship God is in church.	☐	☐
b. I feel close to God when I worship on Sunday morning.	☐	☐
c. I never get anything out of sermons.	☐	☐
d. The songs we sing during the church service help me worship God.	☐	☐
e. The church service helps me live the Christian life during the week.	☐	☐
f. I can invite friends to church without feeling embarrassment.	☐	☐
g. A good worship service should be entertaining.	☐	☐

5 Draw a line connecting the scriptures with the correct statements.

John 4:20-24	**worshiping man**
2 Kings 21:19-22	**worshiping Christ and doubting**
Revelations 4:11	**worship of idols**
Acts 10-25-26	**worship in spirit and truth**
Matthew 28:17	**Christ is worthy**

Date Used: _____

Group: _____

LOOKING UP

Topic: Worship

Purpose of this Session:

Junior high students rarely understand the meaning of worship. They often consider it a boring meeting their parents force them to attend. This TalkSheet provides the opportunity to discuss your church worship service and to encourage your youth group to take their worship service more seriously.

To Introduce the Topic:

Before beginning a disussion using the TalkSheet, conduct a short worship service with your group. Have each division of the service take place in a different room, so you can more easily show the distinctions between the different elements of worship. Include a time of fellowship, singing, prayer, scripture reading, teaching, and offering.

The Discussion:

Item #1: Draw a duplicate of the TalkSheet line on the board and have each student place an X on the line. An alternative would be to draw a chalk line on the floor, from wall to wall. Against one wall is "Always boring", against the other is "Never boring". Have the students stand where they placed their X.

Item #2: Ask the students to share their sentences. (Note: You might wish to show these sentences to your church's worship planning committee. If the students know this in advance, they might come up with more thoughtful responses.) Let them talk about the parts of the service they do not like. Point out some things will be boring but this does not make them bad.

Item #3: Ask the students to share their views on this item and to explain their choices. Ask "What part of our worship service do you enjoy the most? Which part do you think we could do without?"

Item #4: These statements focus on different aspects of worship and the worship service. Let the students debate those in which there is not total agreement. Save your comments for the conclusion.

Item #5: Ask the students to read the way they matched up the verses with the statements. Ask them to share any new insights they might have gained from reading the scriptures on worship.

To Close the Session:

Take this opportunity to present your views on worship and to help your students understand why worship is important. Some ideas: (1) Discuss the concept that worship is a verb, not a noun. It is not something we attend in order to be entertained. Instead, it is something we do. We *worship* God. The worship service helps us do that. (2) The worship service brings everyone in the church together, both young and old, which is important. The church is people, the community of God and it is important for the church to have that common experience together. "Corporate worship" (worship with others) is one way we acknowledge the church is the body of Christ and how much we need each other. (3) Worship is for God, not for us. The question to ask after a worship service is not "Did I like it?" but "Did God like it?" and "Did I do my best for him?"

Close by sharing praise and prayer requests to God.

Outside Activities:

1. Your youth group can plan a worship service. They should be given the freedom to be creative and different. Have them meet with the pastor and congregation members to discuss their ideas.

2. Have volunteers participate in different parts of the morning service, such as scripture reading, ushering, offering, greeting, etc.

3. Ask the pastor or the chairman of the worship committee to come to the youth group meeting and answer questions from the group about your church's worship style.

What Do I Do On Sundays?

List three things you could do on Sunday instead of going to church.

1. _____

2. _____

3. _____

What do you think is the main reason a person should go to church? _____

_____

_____

_____

_____

_____

_____

Do you AGREE or DISAGREE with the statements below?

	AGREE	DISAGREE
a. A person should attend church every week.	☐	☐
b. You can be a Christian without attending church.	☐	☐
c. The church's main concern seems to be taking in money.	☐	☐
d. The church is old-fashioned and out-of-date.	☐	☐
e. It doesn't matter which church you attend.	☐	☐
f. Our church services are boring.	☐	☐
g. I am an important part of our church.	☐	☐

Circle the best answer:

According to Hebrews 10:24-25, attending church is:

a. Optional
b. Unnecessary
c. The way to get to heaven.
d. Habit-forming and encouraging.

Paul, in 1 Corinthians 12:12-14, compares the church to:

a. A body
b. A loaf of bread
c. A fish
d. Heaven

Ephesians 4:16 says church members should:

a. Mind their own business
b. Grow in love
c. Take communion once a week
d. Be critical of each other

WHAT DO I DO ON SUNDAYS?

Topic: The church.

Purpose of this Sesssion:

This TalkSheet was designed to create discussion about the church and to encourage young people to be involved in their church.

To Introduce the Topic:

Ask the students how many Sundays they have gone to church so far. Let them try to figure it out and award a prize to the peson who comes up with the highest number. Have them estimate how many Sundays they will attend church in their entire lifetime.

Share your own earliest recollections of going to church, or read a few selections from the book *101 Things to Do During a Dull Sermon* by Dan Pegoda and Tim Sims (Youth Specialties), or give the students a brief "tour" of the sanctuary (if you are meeting in the church). Use your own creativity as you try to get them to think about the church.

The Discussion:

Item #1: Encourage the students to share the activities they chose to replace church. Talk about the importance or unimportance of each in relation to church attendance. In all probability, many of your junior high students attend church because they are forced to. Ask them, "If you were not forced to go to church, do you think you would still go?"

Item #2: Have the students read all the reasons people should go to church and list them on the blackboard. Have them choose the one they think is the most important. Point out there are many good reasons to attend church.

Item #3: Ask the students to vote on each of these statements according to their answer on the TalkSheet. If everyone is in accord on a particular one, go to the next. If there is a lot of disagreement, let them defend their points of view. Allow them the freedom to express their opinions without your being judgmental. Share your point of view in the conclusion. You might wish to focus on the last statement, because many junior high students feel unnecessary and unimportant to the church. Suggest ways for them to become more involved.

Item #4: Have the students share their answers. Look up the verses and find out if they are correct.

To Close the Session:

As you close this session, you might wish to emphasize the following, as well as other points of your choice:

1. The church is not a building or a service we attend. It is the people of God. When we become a Christian, we become part of the church, the body of Christ.

2. The purpose of the church is not to entertain us nor to provide fun activities. We come to church to learn about God, to grow in faith, and to worship Him. This requires some effort and the desire to do these things.

3. Young people are not the "church of tomorrow". They are an important part of the church of today. Encourage them to get involved in the life of the church. Brainstorm ways they can become more involved.

Outside Activities:

1. Give your group a quiz about the church requiring them to get the answers from other members of the congregation. Sample questions:

a. Name a missionary sponsored by our church, and the country where he or she serves.
b. What is our pastor's middle name?
c. What is the name of our church's newsletter?
d. What year was our church founded?

Struggling

1 Check what you believe about the following subjects:

	RIGHT	WRONG
stealing:	☐	☐
attending church:	☐	☐
talking to your parents about problems:	☐	☐
doing drugs:	☐	☐

2 When you believe something is wrong and you do it anyway . . .

How do you feel? _____

_____

Why do you think you do it anyway? _____

_____

3 Complete the following sentence with the ending most appropriate for you:

I am able to live the way I should _____.

all of the time.   **most of the time.**   **some of the time.**   **none of the time.**

4 Bill knew he shouldn't have cheated on the exam. And this wasn't the first time he had cheated, either. And maybe it won't be the last. Even so, he felt funny about it. It wasn't as if he'd really cheated, since Todd let him look at his answers. Bill concludes what he did wasn't so bad after all, since everybody else does it anyway and nobody is perfect all the time.

What do you think of Bill's behavior? _____

_____

Why did Bill make excuses for what he did? _____

_____

What would you do if you were in Bill's situation? _____

_____

5 Rewrite Romans 7:15 in your own words. _____

_____

_____

_____

STRUGGLING

Topic: Values and behavior

Purpose of this Session:

Adolescence is the time in one's life when there is usually the greatest inconsistency between what one believes and what one does. This TalkSheet is designed to help you discuss the struggles junior high students face as they try to live with their values. It should be used only with a group that interacts well as it requires a deep level of sharing and concern.

To Introduce the Topic:

Have a game of tug-o'-war. This can be done without a rope, if you have the boys sit with their arms and legs locked and let the girls try to pull them apart. Follow this game with the comment, "Trying to live according to our beliefs is a lot like a tug-o'-war. It's a real struggle — as if you are being pulled in two directions. That's what our discussion will be about." Then distribute the TalkSheets.

The Discussion:

Item #1: Have the students share their beliefs on these items. Add others if you wish. Make the point people may believe something but not live it. Ask them which of these beliefs is the most difficult to live. Ask "Can you really believe in something if you don't live it?" Be careful not to ladle a lot of guilt here. Assure them it is normal to believe strongly in something and not be able to live it consistently.

Item #2: Most of the young people will probably say they feel guilty. Point out guilt was designed by God to bring our behavior in line with our values. Explore the "why" question and don't let them get away with "I don't know".

Item #3: Ask if anyone checked "All of the time". If they did, they must believe telling lies is permissable, because they just told one. No one is perfect. We all fail. None of us should be able to live our values and beliefs "none of the time", but our goal should be to live them "most of the time". With God's help, we can.

Item #4: Discuss this "Tension Getter", and ask the students to rank Bill's actions on a scale of 1 to 10, 10 being the best. Most of them will choose a number somewhere in between. Point out life is rarely divided into neat categories, where all our decisions are either black or white, a one or a ten. Sometimes they fall in the middle. We are all a mixture of good and bad and most of life is lived in the grey area. The important thing is to make the wisest decisions possible and to make an attempt to live as we know we should, to the best of our ability. Rationalizing our behavior is not the way, as Bill seems to have done. Ask the students to describe any similar situations they have experienced and what they did.

Item #5: Ask the students to read their paraphrases. Point out Paul felt the same way we do.

To Close the Discussion:

Encourage your students to think through their values and then live as consistently as possible with those values uppermost in their minds. They need to "walk their talk". You might choose a value everyone holds, such as loving their neighbors, and brainstorm a list of pertinent actions to follow-up with during the next week. Encourage them to do that with other values as well. Find ways to put their beliefs into practice, with consistency. The more we do it the right way, the less difficult the struggle the next time.

Stress the fact that failure is normal. But Christ is with us even when we fail. He understands. Commitment to Christ doesn't mean we are perfect. It means when we do fail, we don't give up. We hang in there and Christ has promised to do the same for us.

Thomas Edison made 900 light bulbs before he finally made one that worked. When asked about it, he replied, "Each time I failed, I just discovered one more way not to make a light bulb." We need to have the same attitude about our failures in trying to live the Christian life. We learn what not to do, and keep trying.

Outside Activities:

Have the students search the scriptures for examples of struggling by Biblical characters and find out how they handled their situations and what happened to them. They can then report their findings to the group.

THE HOLY SPIRIT AND YOU

1

Circle any of the words listed below you think best describes the Holy Spirit:

friend	healer	creator	stranger	miracles	temptation
helper	ghost	teacher	counselor	deceiver	electric

2

TRUE or FALSE?

In the Christian faith, the Holy Spirit is not as important as Jesus or God.

_____ **TRUE**   _____ **FALSE**

3

Put a check next to the things listed below you think the Holy Spirit will do for you:

_____ Give you power to live a successful Christian life.

_____ Help you get good grades.

_____ Teach you and help you mature as a Christian.

_____ Give you "spiritual gifts".

_____ Make you better than others.

_____ Help you perform miracles.

_____ Give you peace and comfort.

_____ Help you make the right decisions.

_____ Take away your problems.

_____ Keep bad things from happening to you.

_____ Be your "conscience".

_____ Help you resist temptation.

_____ Give you love for people you don't like.

_____ Give you hope.

_____ Make you feel good inside.

_____ Other: _____.

4

Read Galatians 5:22-26 and list the "fruits of the spirit" below:

a. _____

b. _____

c. _____

d. _____

e. _____

f. _____

g. _____

h. _____

i. _____

Now, put a check mark by the one you need the most.

THE HOLY SPIRIT AND YOU

Topic: The Holy Spirit

Purpose of this Session:

For most junior high students, the concept of the Holy Spirit is a mystery. They can relate to God the Father and God the Son, but they aren't clear about God the Holy Spirit. This TalkSheet gives you the chance to discuss the role the Holy Spirit plays in the life of a Christian.

To Introduce the Topic:

The young people in your group may not understand the Holy Spirit living within them is a storehouse of power that can enable them to live the Christian life. To illustrate, empty a small can of shaving cream on a table top. This will show how much a small can really contains. The same is true for us living as Christians. We are overflowing with God inside us.

The Discussion:

Item #1: Ask the students to share their choices and explain why they were chosen. Don't put anyone down for choosing the "wrong" words. Ask for other suggestions they might use to describe the Holy Spirit.

Item #2: Ask for a show of hands on this True-False question. It will probably get some "true" responses, but again, don't ridicule anyone for not choosing the correct answer, which is "false". This is a good place to explain the doctrine of the Trinity. All three persons of the Trinity are equal because they are the same. They are all God. You may want to consult your church's statement of faith, or look up the following scriptures: John 14:15-31, Romans 8:1-7, I Corinthians 2:6-16.

Item #3: Have the students share their choices. Focus on those things specifically mentioned in the Bible. Here is a partial list: comforts, John 14:16-17; prays for us, Romans 8:26; teaches and guides, John 16:13-15; leads, Galatians 5:18; gives spiritual gifts, I Corinthians 12:7; convicts of sin, John 16:8-11.

Item #4: Ask volunteers to state why they chose one "Fruit of the Spirit" over all the others.

To Close the Session:

Reinforce the important role the Holy Spirit plays in empowering a person to live the Christian life. One way to illustrate this with an object lesson is to use a glove. It cannot do anything without your hand in it. But when you put your hand in the glove, it can do anything your brain wants your hand to do. It can pick up things, wave, scratch your head, and much more. In the same way, when the Holy Spirit is allowed to dwell within us and to work in our lives, we can do anything God wants us to do. Encourage your students to ask God to control their lives more completely.

Outside Activities:

Have your group decide upon three questions they have about the Holy Spirit. They should then try to find the answers to their questions by visiting your church library, browsing a Christian bookstore, talking with the pastor, interviewing the pastor of another church, asking for their parents' viewpoint, etc.

STRESSED OUT

1 "Stress is bad and should be avoided at all costs."

_____ **TRUE** _____ **FALSE**

2 Listed below are some real "stress producers". Check those which would cause a lot of stress for you:

_____ Your parents finding out you lied to them.
_____ Flunking a test.
_____ Hearing our country has declared war.
_____ Getting bad grades on a report card.
_____ Seeing your parents fight.
_____ Being called upon by the teacher when you don't know the answer
_____ Doing something you know is wrong.

_____ Arguing with your brother or sister.
_____ Having no money.
_____ Moving away.
_____ Getting a bad haircut.
_____ Fighting with your parents.
_____ Not having enough time.
_____ Worrying about sex.
_____ Other: _____

3 Answer this question: **What is the best way to get rid of stress?**

_____
_____
_____

4 **Dear Diary:**

Today was horrible! The worst day of my life! I can't believe my problems. Nothing went right. My best friend turned against me. I flunked a social studies test. Everyone laughed at me during P.E. because I was so clumsy. I can't take it anymore. I hate myself. 'Bye for now.

Leslie

Have you ever felt like Leslie? _____

What did you do when you felt like her? _____

_____

What could you tell Leslie to help her feel better? _____

_____

5 Look up one of the scriptures below and decide what it has to say about stress:

Proverbs 3:5,6   **Matthew 6:33,34**   **I Peter 5:7**

_____
_____
_____
_____

STRESSED OUT

Topic: Stress

Purpose of this Session:

Stress is a fact of life to young people as well as adults. Unfortunately, teenagers face an undeserved amount of stress today, most of which was not formerly encountered until adulthood. This TalkSheet will help your group talk about stress and how a Christian can best handle it.

To Introduce the Topic:

Perform a "stress test" on a balloon. Blow it up as far as possible, then blow some more air into it, stressing the surface. If too much pressure is applied, the balloon will pop (demonstrate this if you wish). If you release some of the pressure, the balloon is under less stress.

Make the point that we are like the balloon. If there is too much pressure upon us, we become stressed out. Some people reach the breaking point and that's not good. We need to find ways to relieve the pressure and to reduce stress in our lives. That's what this session is about.

The Discussion:

Item #1: Ask for a show of hands on this True or False question. Explain the best anwer would be "false" because (1) some stress is normal and actually beneficial — the anxiety caused by stress is a warning sytem that helps us respond properly to whatever is causing the stress; and (2) avoidance of all stress is extremely unhealthy. For example, some people turn to drugs or alcohol as a way of escaping stress, which creates even more stress.

Item #2: This activity brings the topic closer to home. Rather than have the students tell you which items they checked, ask "How many of you checked more than three of these? More than five? More than eight?" You can give some sort of "super-stressed" award to the one that checked the most. You might ask the group to vote on the one or two items they think most teens are faced with. Ask them why this is so stressful. Focus on how your students feel when faced with pressures and how they have handled stressful situations.

Item #3: Have the group share their ideas on this. Talk about practical things they can do when they feel overwhelmed by the pressures in their lives.

Item #4: A good way to deal with this "Tension Getter" is to have two students role-play Leslie and a friend who is trying to help her. Or, you can play Leslie and the entire group can advise you. You can give excuses such as "I already tried that" and "That would never work for me", just to keep the ideas generating.

Item #5: Divide the students into smaller groups for this exercise. Each group should take a different Bible verse and come up with a statement about what the Bible says concerning coping with stress.

To Close the Session:

Emphasize the fact that stress is normal, but that unresolved stress can wear them down, both physically and mentally. Stress needs to be dealt with and resolved.

Make sure your students understand if stress, worry, or pressure is getting the best of them, to the point where they are feeling depressed or ill, they must talk to someone about it. Let them know you and other responsible adults are available to listen. Sometimes just talking over a situation can help things get better. A shared load is lighter than one you carry alone.

Help the students realize, too, their parents may be under a great deal of stress at times and they need to be supportive and understanding of them. When their father or mother comes home from work and acts grumpy and upset (and maybe takes it out on them), it might be best for them to stay out of the way and try to be as helpful and positive as they can. Chances are it is just a temporary situation.

Remind your teenagers to set aside time every day to be alone with God. This is not only a great habit to develop, but is a healthy way to handle stress.

Outside Activities:

1. Ask your teens to call three people in their youth group during the coming week and encourage them.

2. Have the students ask their parents how they handle stress as adults and how they handled it as teenagers. They can share what they found out with the group.

DOING DRUGS

1 What is the first thing you think of when you hear the words "doing drugs"? _____

_____

_____

2 Parents should discuss drugs with their kids.

_____ **TRUE**   _____ **FALSE**

3 Jeff and Bill are walking through the park when they see some of their friends smoking marijuana. Jeff and Bill are invited to join in the fun. Jeff says, "Why not, Bill? Let's try it, just this once, to see what it's like! We won't do it again. C'mon! Be a sport, pal!"

If you were Bill, what would you do?

4 Your opinion, please!

	YES	NO	MAYBE
a. Most drugs are harmless.	☐	☐	☐
b. If a friend offered me drugs, I could say no without any problem.	☐	☐	☐
c. If a person's friends are users, then that person needs new friends.	☐	☐	☐
d. Teenagers who use dope are more likely to get into trouble than those who don't.	☐	☐	☐
e. It's okay to use drugs as long as you don't become addicted.	☐	☐	☐

5 Read the following scriptures and write what you think each has to say about using drugs.

I Corinthians 3:16-17 _____

_____

_____

_____

I Corinthians 10:31 _____

_____

_____

_____

Romans 12:1-2 _____

_____

_____

_____

Date Used: _____

Group: _____

DOING DRUGS

Topic: Drugs

Purpose of this Session:

America is a drugged society. Drugs are everywhere, from the medicine cabinet sleeping pills to the cocaine in the executive washroom. Young people, including junior high students, face trememdous pressure to experiment with drugs. Rarely however, do they have the opportunity to discuss the issue in a supportive atmosphere. This TalkSheet will give you a chance to encourage an open discussion about drugs and to emphasize the Christian perspective.

To Introduce the Topic:

Some advance preparation is well worth the effort here. Tape interviews with four to six people about drugs and play the tape for the students. Try to get several differing opinions.

Another good lead-in is to read an article from a magazine or from the newspaper about drug abuse. You won't have to search very far to find a good one. Something local would be preferable (it brings the subject closer to home).

The Discussion:

Item #1: Write the words "Doing Drugs" on the board or on newsprint, visible to all. Underneath, write down all the things offered in response to this question.

Item #2: Ask how many of your group have discussed drugs with their parents and what was said. Encourage your teens to talk with their parents about drugs if they haven't.

Item #3: Use this "Tension Getter" to explain how peer pressure often creates a false need to try drugs. Have the students share their responses to this situation and ask them if they have ever experienced a similar one they would be willing to talk about. You might have them role-play the action, to give them practice in handling a similar occasion.

Item #4: Have the students reveal their answers to these questions with a show of hands. If everyone agrees, move on to the next one. If there is some disagreement, or some doubt, discuss the issue. Allow them to share their responses.

Item #5: You might divide the students into smaller groups and assign one scripture to each. They can then decide as a unit what each passage has to say about drugs, sharing their conclusions with the entire group. Point out the Bible does not specifically mention drugs per se. There is no verse that says "Thou shalt not do drugs", but the scriptures do give us clear principles upon which to make decisions about destructive choices such as drugs.

To Close the Session:

Many young people equate having fun with drug use and/or drinking alcohol. Emphasize there is nothing fun about brain damage, sickness or death, all of which can be the results of drug use. Using drugs is not only illegal, but it is deadly.

Drugs exist because there are people who see nothing wrong with getting rich over the dead bodies and ruined lives of young people. Don't be a sucker. There are better and safer ways to have a good time than "getting loaded and stoned" and wasting your life. Brainstorm with the group a few ways to have fun without using drugs. Emphasize pushers like to get teenagers hooked at an early age, often offering them free drugs for as long as a month, with bonuses for other students they can influence to try them. Once hooked, the victim has no control and the pusher gets what he is after — money. The victim gets permanent brain damage.

Emphasize *all* drugs are harmful and dangerous, even those which are relatively inexpensive and plentiful, like model airplane glue, "liquid paper", "crack" and other chemicals that some teenagers are tying to get stoned on these days.

Point out people generally use drugs because their lives are empty and they erroneously believe drugs will bring them happiness, even if only temporarily. They will most certainly bring them oblivion. Christians, on the other hand, recognize that happiness and peace come only from following Christ.

Let your teenagers know you are willing to talk with them privately if they are having problems with drugs, or if they know someone who is, or if they have questions.

Outside Activities:

Have a few volunteers do some research on the kinds of drugs readily available on the streets. They should find out the street names of the drugs and what effect they have on the body and on behavior. You might want to have an expert visit the group and present some up-to-date information about drugs to your youth group.

Jesus GiVEaWaY

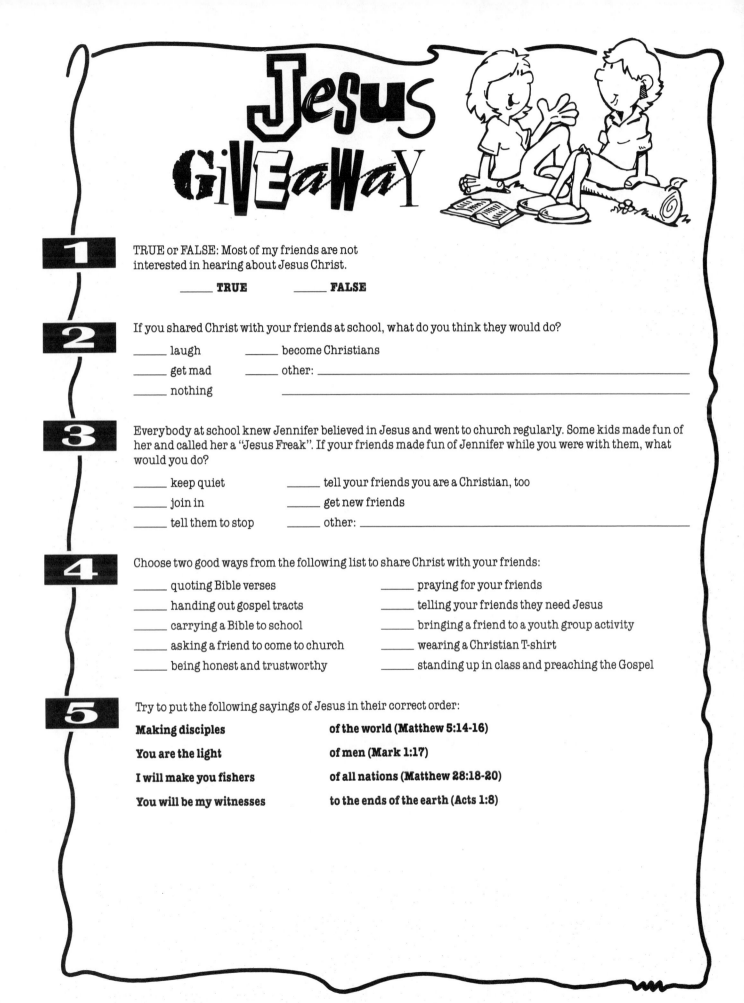

1 TRUE or FALSE: Most of my friends are not interested in hearing about Jesus Christ.

_____ **TRUE**   _____ **FALSE**

2 If you shared Christ with your friends at school, what do you think they would do?

_____ laugh   _____ become Christians

_____ get mad   _____ other: _____

_____ nothing   _____

3 Everybody at school knew Jennifer believed in Jesus and went to church regularly. Some kids made fun of her and called her a "Jesus Freak". If your friends made fun of Jennifer while you were with them, what would you do?

_____ keep quiet   _____ tell your friends you are a Christian, too

_____ join in   _____ get new friends

_____ tell them to stop   _____ other: _____

4 Choose two good ways from the following list to share Christ with your friends:

_____ quoting Bible verses   _____ praying for your friends

_____ handing out gospel tracts   _____ telling your friends they need Jesus

_____ carrying a Bible to school   _____ bringing a friend to a youth group activity

_____ asking a friend to come to church   _____ wearing a Christian T-shirt

_____ being honest and trustworthy   _____ standing up in class and preaching the Gospel

5 Try to put the following sayings of Jesus in their correct order:

Making disciples   **of the world (Matthew 5:14-16)**

You are the light   **of men (Mark 1:17)**

I will make you fishers   **of all nations (Matthew 28:18-20)**

You will be my witnesses   **to the ends of the earth (Acts 1:8)**

Date Used: _____

Group: _____

JESUS GIVEAWAY

Topic: Witnessing

Purpose of this Session:

Most adults have a tough time sharing their faith in Christ so it is no surprise that young people have the same difficulty. This TalkSheet was designed to give you and your group the opportunity to talk about and to practice sharing Christian faith.

To Introduce the Topic:

Pretend aliens from outer space have landed on Earth. They speak English. Divide the group into teams and have each prepare a short speech which one of the team will read to the aliens. The speech should share Christ with the aliens, who have never heard anything about Jesus before. This could also be a role-play, with the alien acting very dumb.

The Discussion:

Item #1: Have the students share and explain their answers. List all the reasons "why not" and all the reasons "why" on a chalkboard or newsprint.

Item #2: After sharing the answers, ask if the students have ever actually tried to share their faith with their friends. If so, what happened? If not, why not?

Item #3: This should make a good role-play subject. Have a few of the students put themselves into this situation and act out their idea of the scenario.

Item #4: Debate the pros and cons of each of the methods listed.

Item #5: Read the verses to find out if the group matched them up correctly. These scriptures emphasize that Christ wants us to tell others about Him.

To Close the Session:

Try to avoid ladling guilt with this session. With their self-esteem on the line, the teenagers will be extremely reluctant to do or say anything that might bring them embarrassment or rejection. Don't make witnessing sound like penance for being a Christian. Help them think of creative ways they can be witnesses for Christ in non-threatening ways. Assure them they do not have to know a lot about the Bible in order to share Christ with others. Nor do they have to be good conversationalists. We can share Christ in a lot of non-verbal ways — by living for Christ in front of our friends.

　　Point out sharing Christ with others is a great privilege as well as a great responsibility. It's giving someone you really care about some really good news.

Outside Activities:

Have the students choose one friend with whom they will share Christ during the next week. They could also choose one other youth group member to pray for as that person shares Christ with a friend.